3⁹⁵

THE CHALLENGE OF HUNGER

THE CHALLENGE OF HUNGER

by

NOËL DROGAT, S.J.

With a Preface by
EDMOND MICHELET

Translated by
J. R. KIRWAN

THE NEWMAN PRESS
WESTMINSTER · MARYLAND

This book is a translation of *Face à la Faim* originally published
by Editions Spes, Paris

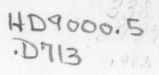

English translation © 1962 Burns & Oates, Ltd.

PRINTED IN GREAT BRITAIN

PREFACE

I BELONG to that group of Europeans of our generation—a large enough group by any count—who have, during long days and months, felt in their own bodies that sharply painful gnawing at the stomach which we believed banished for ever from the west and which is called hunger. Because of this, you have honoured me, an old concentration camp dweller, by asking for some lines of preface to this highly interesting and most moving study of the challenge of hunger.

If we were to rank problems according to their degrees of urgency—to use again a formula which was at one time employed in much less important matters—this one would be ranked first on every count.

As Bernanos has said, this is a century which is filled with paradox; and its most strangely paradoxical aspect lies in that distressing and scandalous contrast to which you point at the very beginning of your work. Never in history does there appear to have been as wide and as deep a ditch between those who lack for nothing and those who have need of everything.

I would not want to be presumptuous and play the specialist while talking superficially on so grave a subject, in which I am a mere layman. Men such as Josué de Castro and, of our own, Père Lebret and Prof. Dumont, have devoted their energies to the study of this tragic problem. I content myself with observing how much you and they seem to have arrived at the right solution in saying, with Colin Clark, that the earth can feed its people. You examine certain African experiments and the decisive evidence of Israel. You look forward to a general extension of educational facilities aimed at the conquest of hunger in the world. Your profound knowledge of farming problems and of rural life qualifies you to offer authoritative and seasonable suggestions for action in this field.

All told, I do not think that I misinterpret your thought in saying that you believe that the multitudes of ill-fed people are in danger of being caught in the totalitarian trap; and that, for their escape from this danger, you look for the establishment of a truly human economy in that part of the world which says it is free and claims to be civilized. Such an economy will not look solely to the profit of the satiated, but will care also and above all for that of the hungry.

There is considerable matter for reflection in the name we gave to our unfortunate comrades in the concentration camps whom hunger had reduced to the fleshless outlines one sees in the *Danse Macabre* of the middle ages. "Musulmen", we called them. There is matter for reflection, too, in the abominable fate reserved for those unfortunates who stole food. One could hold forth at length on the baseness and hyprocrisy of some people in the camps, and the anger, violence and derangement of others. We saw strange settlings of accounts there which, for shame, we kept to ourselves when the day of liberation came.

We are not anxious for a world on which the rage of the starved and the vengeance of the humiliated will impose their rule.

This work of yours will certainly merit numerous readers. I leave to them the task of drawing from it the resolve to act, each in his own way and in the most appropriate manner, so as to avert such a fate. For my part, I am grateful to you, reverend father, for this new opportunity you have given me to go more deeply into the duty which is imposed on every Christian whenever he recites the Lord's Prayer, with its request for daily bread—for us and for all men, our brothers.

EDMOND MICHELET,
Garde des Sceaux,
Ministre de la Justice

CONTENTS

Part I

HUMAN DEMANDS AND FALSE PROBLEMS

Chapter

Part II

THE CONQUEST OF HUNGER

ABBREVIATIONS USED

F.A.O.	Food and Agriculture Organization
I.B.R.D.	International Bank for Reconstruction and Development; or World Bank
I.R.A.M.	Institute for Research into Action against Poverty
I.R.F.E.D.	Institute for Research into Balanced Development
J.A.C.	Young Catholic Farmers
J.A.C.F.	Young Catholic Countrywomen
M.I.J.A.R.C.	International Movement for Young Catholic Farmers and Country dwellers
O.R.A.N.A.	Organization for Research into Food and Nutrition in Africa
U.N.	United Nations
U.N.E.S.C.O.	United Nations Educational, Scientific and Cultural Organization
U.N.I.C.E.F.	United Nations Children's Fund
W.H.O.	World Health Organization

INTRODUCTION

FATHER NOËL DROGAT has done an excellent job in writing this book. I speak from knowledge. I know from experience how difficult it is to give a general appreciation of the problems raised by the standards of nutrition which now obtain in the world. The problem is so complicated and its ramifications so many that an author is in danger either of being superficial and neglecting questions of some importance, or of losing his way in details and wearying his readers with arguments that are too long and too technical.

It is my belief that here the author has avoided both dangers. He has mastered his subject and knows how to see it as a whole. His book is lively, clear, precise and complete.

I have another and very legitimate reason for holding his work in great esteem: it is that the opinions expressed there are in perfect agreement with the conclusions arrived at gradually by F.A.O. during the fifteen years of its existence. Fr Drogat's book takes its place naturally in the plan of action which is being launched under the aegis of our World Campaign against Hunger, of which he speaks in his last chapter.

The principal aim of our campaign is to make people understand the nature of the great economic and social problem of our age and to appeal to the sense of human fellowship, so as, in a word, to awaken consciences.

The problem of hunger will be solved only when the countries which breed poverty shall have succeeded in making a substantial improvement in their agricultural production. This is by no means the only solution: but it is by far the most important. It cannot be denied that the resources of land and sea are not being used as they could be. But there are two conditions which must be satisfied if more is to be produced: the farmer must have the aptitude to work harder and better; and he must have the tools to enable him to do so. The poor countries will not be able to satisfy both of these conditions within a reasonable time, unless the nations which are in the van of progress help them for as long as may be necessary. This must be done in two ways. First, to equip agriculture and particularly to re-arrange farms, apply land reforms and set up institutions of various sorts: and second, to educate the farmers, gain their confidence, create rural leadership and furnish the countryman with that frame of reference without which he will be unable to undertake anything with any chance of success.

There is not one man among us, of whatever station in life, to whom the existing state of affairs is of no concern. We are all of us bound to those who are hungry, whether we like it or not.

It is for this reason that we must unite our efforts, paying no attention to frontiers, and work with all our will and all our might. The need is urgent and will persist for a long time.

We can expect to get the desired results. I could ask for no better proof of this than the promising results obtained already by F.A.O. But its means, alas, are much too few. That is the reason why it has launched its world campaign.

M. VEILLET-LAVALLÉE,
Asst. Director-General,
F.A.O.

Part One

Human Demands
and
False Problems

I

THE BITTER PARADOX

To close one's eyes to what has been called "the tragedy of the century"[1] is quite impossible. Here is mankind, split in two, torn apart in body and in soul. Cheek by jowl with a small minority, well endowed and well fed, live two thousand million men who are sunk in wretchedness.

On one side, we have the under-developed countries, deprived of all that is comprised in modern civilization, lacking the conveniences of life and of comfort and without facilities for education and for leisure. On the other side is the western world, which every day gains more advantage from the perpetual growth which issues from its scientific techniques and—this must be admitted—its methodical and persistent work. For the economies of the West, increasing productivities and merciless competition are strikingly effective incentives.

The gap has never been so wide between "those who lack for nothing" and "those who want everything".[2]

This gap does not exist only in matters of medicine, education, industrial capital and means of transport. It exists also in the sphere of agriculture, where output becomes less and less adequate for the increasing numbers of people. To quote R. Scheyven: "Before the war, 38 per cent of the world's population did not have enough to eat: now, 59·5 per cent are in that condition. It is an astonishing fact that, despite our inventions and our modern techniques, we cannot assure that many more than 40 per cent of the population will have enough to eat."[3]

There is the fact. Hundreds of millions of men are hungry.

At the Angers *Semaine Sociale*, M. André Piettre summed up the position in a few words: "Economic growth tends to

[1] R. P. Lebret, *Le Drame du Siècle* (1960).
[2] Cf. Noël Drogat, *Pays sous-développés et Coopération techni que* (1959).
[3] Quoted from *Pensée Chrétienne et Communauté mondiale.*

make the rich richer, while population growth tends to make the poor poorer."

That is the problem which confronts the world today.

It cannot possibly be said that things were better managed in the past. Throughout history, innumerable famines have been as milestones on man's journey. Some have been so severe as to decimate whole peoples; others have been no worse than bad harvests, limited often to particular areas. From the days of the Ptolemys in Egypt until today, man has periodically suffered this calamity and has lacked the means to avert it.

Low productivity and bad communications made the problem virtually insoluble. In the world of yesterday, split up into separate compartments, one bad harvest due to drought or flood was enough to cause distress throughout a region. What small reserves existed were soon exhausted; and even when there were some stocks of foodstuffs they could be brought in only with difficulty. There was no alternative to cutting rations. Such were the means of transport, whether by land or by sea, that but little help could be looked for from without.

It is difficult for us to imagine what living conditions could be like in former times. Around the year 1000 A.D., at the time of the Great Famine, countries in the West went through periods of extreme want which were marked, in some places, by the re-emergence of untamed instincts. People gathered what they could for food: acorns, roots, grass, leaves. Crushed reeds and rushes were used for making porridge. Some people were reduced to eating the bark of trees and thatch from the roofs. The tale of Tom Thumb and the giant who ate children was not altogether fictional. Chroniclers of the time furnish us with convincing details. Folk did not always content themselves with robbing the traveller: sometimes there were other explanations for his disappearance, reasons into which it would be repugnant for us today to look more closely.

During the sixteenth century France suffered thirteen periods of general dearth. There were hard times during the reigns of Louis XIV and Louis XVI and several insurrections, when the peasants boiled grass to eat. Food was scarce in 1810 and 1811, under Napoleon: at the time of the Restoration, Madame de Rémusat speaks in her memoirs of the worries of her husband, then prefect of the Haute-Garonne, whose task it was to avert a famine.

Southern and Central Europe fared no better. There were bad famines in Italy and in Spain; and during hard times in Russia and Poland people were reduced to grinding straw mixed with acorns and leaves to make bread. England, also, experienced periods of intense want in the course of its history.

However, it has always been in Asia and the Middle East where people have suffered most from hunger. In his book, *China, the Land of Famine*, Mallory lists more than ninety famines in one century. He estimates that during the nineteenth century alone, more than one hundred million Chinese died of hunger. India has always been the scene of deadly famines. In this over-populated region which is so dependent on the caprice of the monsoon, millions of people die of want. There were five millions of them in 1876: and in 1899 the British government was able to bring relief to only five out of fifty million hungry people. A million and a half died. In 1868, the Near East was struck by this scourge, particularly Arabia, where 300,000 people died.

The Russian famine of 1921–22 decimated the population, killing several million people. According to a report published by the League of Nations in 1924, there were instances of cannibalism, particularly in the Volga region.[4]

Examples could be multiplied, some of them very close to us. Such were the "march of the hungry" in north-east Brazil in 1958, when people were driven from their homes by a long drought and died of exhaustion at the roadside. Nevertheless, it is certain that the gravest dangers can be averted today, thanks to better means of communication and the existence of stock-piles of surplus products.

What is the position now with regard to the world problem of food, which closely affects not only the existence of millions of people, but also the maintenance of peace? Despite the efforts made since the last world war to increase the output of agricultural produce, many parts of the world are still haunted by the spectre of hunger and malnutrition.

Only one-sixth of the people in the world can satisfy their hunger. This situation, already out of balance though it be, is in

[4] League of Nations: *Report on Economic Conditions in Russia* (1924).

danger of being made worse by the growth of population, unless urgent attention is given to the task of correcting so grave a disequilibrium.

The F.A.O. report published in 1959, *The World's Food and Agricultural Situation*, is particularly instructive in this connection. It brings out the distortion that exists between the growth of production and the actual levels of feeding of the greater part of mankind.

On one hand, the report considers the growth of agricultural production in the world, which, in 1958–59, was twice as great as the growth of population. While world population was increasing by 1·6 per cent, agricultural production grew by 4 per cent. However, this growth in output was for the most part in countries which were well-equipped, where already the people had enough to eat and where there was little scope for extending consumption.

On the other hand, the report considers the low levels of feeding over the greater part of the globe, where peoples often have supplies which are too poor, whether judged by quantity or by quality. Statistics are advanced to show that, while Latin America, the Far East, the Near East and Africa have between them three-fifths of the world's population, they dispose of only one-third of the world's agricultural production.

We do well to bear in mind that these figures give us only a general order of magnitude. The difficulties which lie in the way of using figures collected in under-developed countries, which have not as yet an administrative machine capable of doing such work, are well known.

At the same time, there is no room for believing that these official findings do not describe, in general, a state of affairs which does actually exist. The conclusion is self-evident. Today, there is more food in the world, yet most men do not eat better. There are some parts, indeed, which are in a worse situation from this point of view than they were in 1938.

For the most part, the purchasing power of the under-developed countries has grown but little. In consequence, these countries cannot import, from lands having a surplus, supplies of agricultural products large enough to meet their most urgent needs. On their side, the countries where output is excessive are often embarrassed by the existence of large stocks which depress both domestic and foreign markets.[5]

The paradoxical side of the situation is illustrated by the fact that during that period (1958–59), and principally in North America, stocks rose by 12 per cent. M. Ezekiel, director of the economic section of the F.A.O., used the occasion to emphasize the point: "There are thousands of individuals who will suffer from hunger and malnutrition throughout their lives; and yet there are immense stocks of cereals and other foodstuffs which are never used."

We must in justice point out that these stocks have often in the past proved of great use in relieving particular countries stricken by a bad harvest. It is not many years since this was the case with India, Pakistan and Morocco. American wheat was sent, almost always as a gift, to these countries in need.

Yet, as Mr B. R. Sen has pointed out in this F.A.O. report: "However appreciable this contribution may be, it is none the less true that, in the long run, the problem created by the hungry lands and the insufficiency of supplies of foodstuffs in the under-developed countries can only be resolved by the modernization of agriculture in those areas. It is, therefore, essential to discover what economic, social and technical reforms are necessary for that purpose. Until that is done, the agricultural populations of many under-developed countries will continue to suffer a poverty such as the inhabitants of richer lands can scarcely imagine, their food supplies will continue to be precarious and general economic progress will be greatly impeded."

[5] In order to relieve this situation and also to aid the development of the World Campaign against Hunger, the Council of the F.A.O. in November, 1960, adopted a resolution recently passed by the General Assembly of the United Nations. This resolution asked that measures be taken to bring about a better distribution and utilization of surplus supplies of foodstuffs. The F.A.O. tried to find practical ways and means and to ascertain:

1. Mutually acceptable methods and conditions which would make available the largest possible quantity of foodstuffs;

2. The additional arrangements which would have to be made to put these foodstuffs at the disposal of the worst-provided regions. One very important use for surplus foodstuffs would be to provide for workers who were employed in development projects, or who were being trained for such projects. Cf. the 1955 F.A.O. study on *The Utilization of Excess Supplies of Agricultural Produce to Finance the Development of Economically Underdeveloped Countries.* Cf. also N. Drogat, *Économie Rurale et Nourriture des Hommes*, p. 260.

Through the amazing progress of science and technology man is coming to possess an ever increasing mastery over nature. If we were to draw a graph of technical progress, we would see that, after having remained virtually horizontal for centuries, the curve had suddenly taken a leap and begun rapidly to climb almost vertically, pushed on by a sort of cumulative progression.

It is thought by some people that mankind has reached a new stage of development, in view of the power which it commands from electronics and automation to the enormous potential of atomic energy. It is possible for man to tame the swiftest rivers, to water the deserts, to create new inland seas and to change, as it were, the face of entire regions. Why is it, then, that eminently useful projects, such as restoring fertility to desert lands, are often held back, so as to make way for more spectacular, but considerably less profitable, ventures?

We are moving too fast, and in the wrong direction, writes Robert Guillain: "Will not the passion of the West for the systematic application of research to advance the course of technical progress result in the creation of a world apart, a world of selfish ease and artificial prosperity to which the majority of men will have no access? While we are building our atomic piles, in Brazil the consumption of tallow—a certain indicator of rural stagnation—is increasing. While we are making electronic robots, the scythe, a simple implement, is almost unknown in India. Could we be so naive as to believe that the astounding technical progress in the most advanced countries will bring an automatic, and timely, remedy for the ills from which the backward countries suffer?"

It would be absurd, of course, to seek to stop progress. Yet, surely, in the utilization of techniques there is some order of priority to observe. Preference should be given to those which have for their purpose the satisfaction of man's essential needs: food, clothing, housing, health. In this sphere, it would appear that not all has been done that could have been done. Could not the great investment called for by the development of atomic missiles or the preparations for space travel, for example, have been used to finance schemes for agricultural modernization or irrigation in the most under-privileged regions? Rather than indulge in a politics of prestige, ought men not to observe an order of urgency in the commitment of resources?

The world knows well enough how enormous have been the sums swallowed up in the modern armaments race between East and West, in the effort to maintain a balance of terror. Even when it is produced on a considerable scale, a submarine equipped with Polaris missiles costs the Americans more than one hundred million dollars. The programme for a fleet of nuclear submarines had already up to June, 1960, cost two thousand seven hundred million dollars. Everybody knows that the Russians, on their side, devote a sum at least as large to the same ends.

If, instead of being too often misused to damage or destroy, the resources of the modern industrial economy had been used, as Bergson asked, to guarantee provision for essential human needs, there would be less suffering in the world and also, beyond a doubt, less menacing a threat from political and social stress.[6]

At the end of a journey around the world, Norris E. Dodd, the Director-General of F.A.O., said in 1949: "Everywhere I have been, whether in Asia and the Far East, or Latin America and the Near East, the difficulties I found had their roots in poverty and privation, hunger and malnutrition. I found families whose full store of linen was one sheet. When one member of the family left the home or went into town, that sheet served for clothing; and meantime the other members of the family stayed indoors, naked, with not a stitch to cover them. Everywhere, prices rise and hunger sits at the hearth of millions of people. Here is a match to light the flames of war."

Others raise their voices in the same strain. "Hunger is a greater danger for the future of mankind than is the atomic

[6] The words of the great philosopher have a profound simplicity and strength. He sketches the characteristics essential to a political economy which would think rather of men than of profit. "There are times when we must take a broad view. Millions of men have not enough to eat. Some even die of hunger. If more were produced, there would be much less risk of people being short of food. We feel strongly that agriculture, by which men eat, ought to rank above all else, and be, in any case, the first care of industry itself. In general, industry is not sufficiently mindful of the relative importance of various wants. It is content to follow fashion, making only that which it thinks will sell. In this case, as in others, we could wish for a general design, a plan, which would co-ordinate industry and agriculture, giving to machines their proper function, that of rendering the greatest possible service to mankind." (Bergson, *Les Deux Sources de la Morale et de la Religion*, p. 330.)

bomb", says Lord Boyd Orr. And Harold Wilson, in his book *The War on World Poverty*, puts the same thought in another way: "The most pressing problem for the greater part of mankind is neither war, nor communism, nor the cost of living, nor taxes: it is hunger. This is because hunger is at the same time the effect and the cause of the poverty and suffering which afflict one thousand five hundred million human beings."

Suffering humanity's ancient dream of food enough for all can be made to come true tomorrow. It is for us to decide. The outcome depends upon the technical and financial help which we are prepared to bring to those peoples who are not able by themselves to break out of the vicious circle of poverty, ignorance and hunger.

It is the view of the most competent international and technical experts that, if we were to use on the required scale the resources at our command today, it would be possible not only to maintain the present level of nutrition in the world, despite the growth of population, but also to raise it appreciably. For it is in the under-developed countries that agriculture, using traditional techniques of low productivity, affords the greatest scope for progress.

There are many parts of the world where human malnutrition would cease to be a problem if methods which could raise output sufficiently were universally practised. Such improved farming techniques as cross-breeding and the use of better vegetable and animal strains, soil analysis and treatment with natural and artificial manures, and irrigation and drainage would do this for the more backward countries. But it is clear, for example, that wherever the fertilizer industry could be established it would demand preference for aid and development from government planning.

All doors are now open in every department of applied agricultural science. The limits of what is possible are enlarged with every day that passes. There is a steady flow of new discoveries, some of which may be found to be revolutionary. Never before have there been such good grounds for hope that production can be increased enough to meet men's needs.

However, there is still something lacking. Before all these resources can be brought to the service of mankind, there must be a universal intention to co-operate effectively. A great step towards the abolition of hunger will have been taken when the nations agree to replace ballistics research, launching pads and the armaments race with a far-reaching scheme of agricultural research stations and experimental farms and a healthy spirit of emulation among scientists of every land. That day may not be very far away.

Poverty is "neither God's command nor nature's law", says François Perroux. It is legitimate nowadays to see in a well-balanced technique an immense power for the freedom of mankind. It is thanks to it that the world is on the road to re-unification, that the oneness of our globe begins to acquire a meaning, for now the world is truly conscious of its own existence. As someone has said: "A new and real community is formed, which makes us in some sort 'citizens of the world' and brings close to us those who, in former times, were furthest removed."[7]

Pope John XXIII spoke in similar terms when he addressed delegates from international organizations at the opening of the World Campaign against Hunger. "We must awaken consciences to a sense of the responsibilities which weigh on each and every one, and particularly on those who are most well-off. We live today in a world where distance no longer matters. No man can make the excuse that he is ignorant of the needs of his brother far away or that it is no concern of his to bring help. We are all jointly responsible for the under-fed."

[7] Albert Dondeyne: discussions at the Catholic Centre for French Intellectuals on "Technology and Man" (June 1960).

Speaking in December, 1959, at the opening of the American pavilion at the world farming exhibition at New Delhi, President Eisenhower declared that it was possible to end hunger. "We have the knowledge now to banish at least this scourge from the world, this hunger which debilitates the bodies of children, afflicts the hearts of parents and unloosens the passions of those who work without respite to gain a niggardly livelihood. Today, men have knowledge and resources enough to declare war on hunger throughout the world and to win the victory. That kind of war dignifies and exalts mankind."

II

IS THERE AN INSUFFICIENCY OF LAND?

ARE those people right who say that soon the earth will be unable to feed the human family, grown too large? The demographic explosion of modern times has frightened more than one scholar or investigator who worries about the future of our planet.

The main figures are well known. Beginning from 1650, it took two hundred years for the world population to double. From 1850, it took one hundred years to double again. During the first half of the twentieth century it has grown by 60 per cent and, at the present rate of growth, it will double again in the second half.

The demographic section of U.N. has recently had cause to revise the forecast it made in 1954. Taking the mean of the estimates prepared (and they assume a considerable fall in the birth-rate in a number of countries after 1975), it has arrived at the conclusion that the world will have 3,000,000,000 inhabitants in 1962, 4,000,000,000 by about 1977, 5,000,000,000 by about 1990, and 6,000,000,000 before the end of the century.

Every million added to the population call for the addition to world supplies of some 13,000,000 tons of cereals and 14,000,000 tons of animal products (meat, milk, fish and eggs). This is an indication of the intense effort which will be found to be necessary in the near future.[1]

Will world food supplies increase at the same rate as population? Will there be cultivable land enough to feed so many people?

In the face of these questions, a forced optimism is not good enough. The fate of hundreds of millions of men is too grave a

---

[1] If we take into account the increase in the level of nutrition which is necessary, we find that by 1980 the production of cereals will have to be increased by about 30 per cent, while the supply of animal products will need to be almost doubled. (M. Wright, *Symposium of the British Association*, 1960.)

matter. On the other hand, it must be said firmly that a pessimism which is convinced in advance that the world is moving to disaster does not appear to be any more justified.

We cannot but be aware of the heated debates on this subject in which authorities have engaged at numerous assemblies, to say nothing of the flood of items published on it in the press.

Books such as William Voigt's *Road to Survival* and Fairfield Osborn's *Our Plundered Planet* made a great impression on anglo-saxon opinion. They dramatized the effects of wasteful farming techniques, pointing to an exhaustion of resources while populations went on increasing. According to Voigt: "Only one-quarter of the dry land is cultivable, and we are already farming two-thirds of the land that can be exploited. Our reserves of minerals and of power are being used up. . . . We are not making progress, but running on disaster, to the extent that we are failing to check the mounting flood of overpopulation." The method he advocates is the limitation of births and the inauguration of a politics of birth-control.

More recently there has appeared in France the work of A. Guerrin,[2] which attempts to draw up a detailed balance-sheet showing, somewhat theoretically, the maximum possibilities of growth of the world's food supplies. It puts into the scales the lands as yet unused, increases in yields and improvements in methods of storing foodstuffs: while it takes account, on the other side, of expected losses from erosion and soil impoverishment and the ever growing loss of farm land to the towns. At the end of his enquiry, M. Guerrin found himself unable to share the confidence of those who refuse to think of controlling the world population systematically, so as to check its rate of growth.

This serious matter was debated in April, 1960, at an international meeting at Vevey. On that occasion, Prof. M. Mathey, Rector of the University of Lausanne, had no hesitation in asserting: "Famine on a large scale lies in wait for mankind." And, he added, "the method in which help is now being given to the under-developed countries is leading the white people to race suicide. The aid constitutes a process of selection in a mass of humanity in which the white race is becoming a progressively smaller part".

[2] André Guerrin, *Humanité et subsistances*, 1957.

The debate is not one-sided. To facts and figures put forward from one side, other facts and figures are advanced by the other. Colin Clark, for example, after examining the main features of the problem, came to this categorical conclusion: "The material resources of the world would easily suffice to make such provision [a satisfactory livelihood], not only for the whole human race as it now is, but for any conceivable expansion of our numbers which is likely to occur for a very long time." In his view, the often under-used resources at our disposal are potentially capable of feeding 28,000,000,000 people—ten times the number now living. This figure could be trebled if mankind's diet were to be based exclusively on cereals.[3]

Authorities attached to F.A.O. have had wide experience and dispose of a mass of information on this subject. They consider that most of the misunderstandings which mark the course of the debate on the continued feeding of an increasing population arise out of our imperfect knowledge of the earth's potentialities, plus the idea, widely held in some quarters, that the soil is being rapidly exhausted. As regards the last point, it is pointed out that, if soils can be exhausted through improvidence and defective farming methods, they can also be rehabilitated and improved if the appropriate measures are taken. The state of Israel affords a striking proof of this, for there life has been brought back to land that had been made into a desert. As regards extension of the cultivable areas, there are certainly considerable possiblities; but here it might be necessary to take a long view because of the heavy investment which such projects would often require.

Officials of F.A.O. have come to a firm conclusion. "In principle, the farmers of the world would be able to produce enough food to conquer hunger. They will have to modernize their equipment and methods, particularly in the under-developed regions; but this requires that modern science be put at the disposal of all nations, and not only, as it is today, at the disposal of the more prosperous of them."[4] Leaving out of account none of the difficulties which stand in the way, whether

[3] Colin Clark, "The Earth can feed its People," in *World Justice*, Sept. 1959, p. 35.

[4] F.A.O. *Man and Hunger*, p. 19.

they spring from political, social, cultural or economic factors, the effects of which cannot be exactly foreseen, they conclude that any prophecy in this field can be made only conditionally and cautiously.

According to the U.N. 1960 annual survey of population,[5] each year about 100 million children are born and 51 million people die. Each year, world population increases by more than 48 million, a number somewhat larger than the whole population of France.

The U.N. demographers warn us to expect an even larger annual increase. The rate of increase tends itself to increase, because the number of people in the procreative age groups rises every year. At the same time, the extent of the control secured over the epidemic diseases, such as malaria and tuberculosis, is already great enough appreciably to reduce mortality, even in the most backward parts of the world.

[5] Most of the figures in this chapter are taken from this publication.

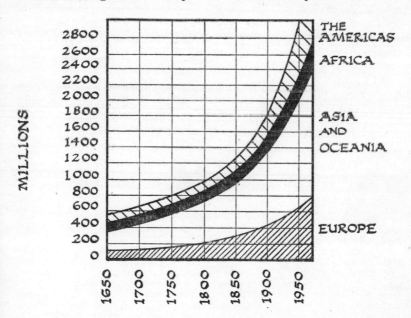

GROWTH OF POPULATION SINCE 1650

It is important, also, to bear in mind that it is in the under-developed countries that population is rising most rapidly today. The rate of growth there is 2 or 3 per cent. In some places it is even greater: e.g. the Ivory Coast has a rate of 5·3 per cent; Upper Volta and Costa Rica, 4 per cent; Syria, 3·9 per cent; Salvador, 3·5 per cent; Honduras, 3·3 per cent. In the most advanced countries, on the other hand, the rate of growth is often less than one per cent. Europe, the most densely populated continent, has a growth rate of only 0·7 per cent.

The causes of this sudden upward thrust of population are in no way mysterious. In former times, a natural equilibrium between food supplies and people to be fed was maintained by a rate of high infantile mortality, epidemics and wars. Today, advances in methods of medicine and hygiene have broken the ancient balance. In many parts of the world, birth rates remain at the traditional level of forty to fifty per thousand of population, while death rates go on falling.

Nor is there any reason to expect an appreciable fall in the birth rates of the under-developed countries, particularly in Africa, South America and Asia (with the exception of Japan).[6] People in these areas marry young or often practice polygamy and where the economy has remained at subsistence level children are thought of primarily as extra hands. Furthermore, it was at one time necessary to beget ten children if three were to be reared successfully. There is now a new fact to face: fewer children die. As Pierre Gouron has put it, what we see in

[6] What information we have about India reveals a not inappreciable fall in the death-rate, unaccompanied by any fall in the birth-rate, although among the educated classes the government's campaign for family planning seems to be having some effect. Contraceptive propaganda, which is approved by New Delhi though it may not be encouraged, does not seem as yet to have had much effect on the mass of the people.

Japan has been applying a systematic policy of "birth-control" both through contraception and abortion, since the end of the second world war. It is one of the few countries in which the birth-rate has fallen sharply, dropping from 34·3 per thousand in 1947 to 17·2 per thousand in 1957. The Japanese population continues to increase, but the rate of growth seems now to have been stabilized at about 0·7 per cent. The Chinese Peoples' Republic has been pursuing a more complicated population policy. At first, it advocated methods of limiting births after the Japanese example and contrary to the principles affirmed by the communist bloc; of late, however, it appears to be pursuing an opposite policy. Be that as it may, with its present rate of growth the population of China could exceed 1,000,000,000 by the end of this century.

these countries is a mediaeval birth-rate associated with a modern death-rate.

In the years to come, therefore, we can expect to see a widening gap between the advanced and the under-developed countries. The growth of population in the latter will tend to change the balance in world affairs, as can be verified already at the meetings of the U.N. Assembly. Figures set out by U.N. organizations give us an idea of the scale of the change, on both a medium and a long term view. The under-developed lands (Africa: Central America and the tropical zone of South America: the Pacific Islands, apart from Australia and New Zealand) had populations totalling 1,640 millions in 1950. They can be expected, at a moderate estimate, to have 2,660 millions in 1975 and nearly 4,800 millions by the year 2000. On the other hand, the population of the more advanced lands, and particularly that of Europe, will increase much more slowly. Whereas now there is one European for two Asiatics, by the end of this century we may see one for four.

Does this process of change indicate that the ancient equilibrium between man and the earth has been irremediably impaired? Will a better utilization of their own soil enable the developing countries to meet the new needs of their young populations? The conclusions to which our enquiry will lead us will enable us, we believe, to answer the question to some extent.

To begin with, it would be quite incorrect to speak of a danger of over-population, as though what we had to deal with were a generalized phenomenon. We ought not to underrate the importance of the uneven way in which mankind is distributed around the globe. These differences in population density are due in part to climatic conditions and to the character and potentialities of soil and natural resources, in part to political conditions.

The most densely peopled continent is Europe, with 218 persons to the square mile. (This is including Russia, which has no more than 26 persons to the square mile.) Next comes Asia, with 151 to the square mile: 115 in the south-east and 167 in the east of the continent. America has only 23 to the square mile: 23 in the north, 20 in the south, and 59 in the centre of the continent. Last of all is Africa, with only 20 to the square mile.

It is true that in the monsoon lands of Asia there are areas where the population is extraordinarily dense. While countless crowds are packed into the alluvial plains, immense areas are almost uninhabited. Population density is very high in certain parts of South-east Asia—it is 3,800 to the square mile on the paddy fields of the Tonkin delta—in India, in China and even in Europe, and these regions pose special problems. Nevertheless, it can be stated that over the greater part of the world population is still far short of its optimum level, given that many areas do not have more than 25 to 40 people to the square mile. This is the situation in most parts of Africa and of South America (Brazil, in particular), and in certain parts of Asia where there are lands which could be made productive.

Apart from this, the word itself, "over-population", is susceptible of different interpretations. For any particular part of the world, it could mean the difference between the size of the population that exists and that which can be fed from local produce: but it could also be given a wider meaning, taking into account the possibilities there are of ensuring for the people employment and a sufficiency of purchasing power. Ten people in a part of the Sahara larger than Corsica might constitute over-population, whereas Hong-Kong, with 6,900 people to the square mile, can provide for its population by trade.[7]

In a recent study of the evolution of ideas on "over-population", A. Sauvy has shown how outmoded is the former static concept, which applied particularly to agricultural economies on a largely subsistence level. He cites the example afforded by West Germany since 1945. On restricted lands, provision has there been made for a large population which has been quickly added to by the flood of refugees from East Germany. This has been done by means of intensified industrial development; a typical case, M. Sauvy observes, of population growth with no extension of territory being required.[8]

An area, however limited, can well support a dense population provided that there are industrial, commercial and other

[7] Speaking of the polar regions where hunting and fishing provide the only means of subsistence, Colin Clark says "it has been estimated that the Eskimos and Red Indians of north-western Canada require on the average 55 square miles per head of their cold tundra to provide adequate hunting ground". (l.c. p. 37).

[8] "The most optimistic forecasts regarding West Germany have been surpassed by events. Between 1950 and 1958, the population gainfully employed

activities which will enable its inhabitants to obtain from outside the food which cannot be grown at home. To the extent that this is possible, the point of over-population is pushed back. We have examples of this ,in highly industrialized countries with advanced techniques, such as Germany, England, Belgium and Switzerland, which have to import a considerable part of their food supplies. The same possibilities do not exist, however, for densely populated areas which are only now beginning to be developed, such as India, China and certain Pacific and South American countries. These countries lack purchasing power and so are compelled to depend upon their own soil for the greater part of their food supplies.

There are some densely populated countries where it seems particularly difficult to arrive at a balance between man and his environment and which, therefore, call for particular attention.

First among these is India, where the soil is often exhausted and the climate is debilitating, which forms in itself a sub-continent as large as Europe outside Russia, and where one person in three suffers from malaria. It has some 400,000,000 inhabitants, at an average density of 308 to the square mile. Its people are still held in a net of religious and social traditions, which constitute a very serious brake on the attempts at modernization which the government has launched since the gaining of independence.

Today, the population of India grows by 2 per cent each year, or about 8,000,000 persons, as against 5,000,000 in 1951. Since the birth rate remains high, at 40 per thousand, the population has every likelihood of growing from 400,000,000 in 1959 to 460,000,000 in 1966, the year in which the third of the five-year plans is due to end. The feeding of these multitudes of townspeople and country dwellers, already under-fed, is in danger of becoming quite insufficient, unless there is an enormous increase in the output of the cereals and vegetables

(*continued from p.* 18)
(we except those unemployed) has grown by 4,701,000. Since 1939 the active population has increased by more than 6,500,000. This growth has not extended to the farm population, for that has declined by about 800,000. It has been concentrated in industry, trade and the public services; that is to say, on activities calling for little space and even, in some cases, for little in the way of raw materials." ("Evolution récente des idées sur le surpeuplement": *Population*, June-July, 1960: p. 471.)

on which the Indian diet is based. "Unless production grows more quickly than it has done of recent years, the difference between supplies and requirements will be about 28,000,000 tons in 1965–6."[9]

However difficult it may be to increase production sufficiently in existing conditions, technical authorities, such as René Dumont, do not consider the task to be impossible.[10] The greater part of the agricultural land is so under-developed and relatively unproductive that there exists considerable scope for development, if the right means are used. At the time of his journey to India, Pierre Gascar, who had been struck by the under-developed state of the fields, wrote: "The yield of corn in India is at present 10 to 15 bushels to the acre, whereas in Western Europe it is 40. The yield of rice in India is 26 bushels to the acre, but in Japan it is 75. It should not be held a fault in human beings to be numerous and there does not, in fact, exist a problem of over-population. The lack of balance between the peoples and their resources is but temporary: the earth is only a little way behind life."[11]

The agricultural potential of India is far from being realized, not only as regards yields, but also as regards cultivable area. The problem is one of improvement. It is estimated that since the inauguration of the five-year plans, India has spent as much on the importation of foodstuffs as on its industry. There is need for a greater effort directed to the modernization of its agriculture.

The case of China is somewhat different. There, every piece of fertile soil has always been put to what could be called the maximum use, being worked by a peasantry that is steady and hard-working and makes careful use of techniques that give relatively high yields. The bond between the peasant and his land—in a fierce struggle with devastation and calamity— has allowed the establishment of a precarious equilibrium built on habits of care and on privation. The people of China

[9] Ford Foundation: *Report on India's food crisis and steps to meet it.* (New Delhi, Government of India Press, 1959.)

[10] On his return from a recent visit to India, M. Dumont stated that the agricultural situation was far from desperate. "In most of the areas visited, there is a way—often narrow and full of traps, but none the less perceptible— which can lead to progress."

[11] Pierre Gascar, *Voyage chez les vivants,* p. 185.

today do not enjoy abundance, but nor do they die of hunger.[12]
What has the future in store for the population of China?
It is now 660,000,000 and each year adds 15,000,000, a number
approximately equal to the population of Canada. U.N.
forecasts, based on assumptions that the birth rate will stay
high while the death rate will fall, indicate that the population
could reach 1,287,000,000 in 1983. A more conservative estimate
would put the figure at 1,000,000,000. That is to say, twenty
years from now one-quarter of humanity will be Chinese.

Even so, in China there is no lack of land which can be
made productive. The present government is doing its best
in this direction by directing migration to the much more
sparsely inhabited lands of the north and west. However, the
most tempting areas for colonization lie beyond the existing
frontiers of China, a fact which explains the aggressive policies
of the Pekin government. It is now laying claim to territories
which formerly, in the more or less distant past, formed part
of the Celestial Empire. Today, it is Tibet and Nepal. Tomorrow
it will be the turn of parts of Mongolia and Manchuria, now
under Russian control but which were at one time joined to
China. There are enormous habitable areas in Siberia which are
extremely thinly peopled—Siberia has only 18 persons to the
square mile—while in China the pressure of population mounts
and the need for space becomes more strongly felt. As has been
said, "It could well be that a large part of tomorrow's history
has already been written in the statistics of population."

Japan is not an under-developed country, but it is over-
populated, having 92,000,000 people and extremely little
cultivable ground. It can hardly be compared at all with the
regions we have just examined. Industry is very advanced,
as are also the technical skills of managements and wage-
earners. These, together with an intensive agriculture and large
scale fishing industry, afford the Japanese people a standard of

[12] Reporting recently on the Chinese Peoples' Republic, Tibor Mende notes
that the efforts demanded from the peasants seem to have pushed back the
risk of famine. "The whole Chinese people is certainly obliged to work
extremely hard and their persons are completely at the disposal of the state
throughout the day. Nor can it be denied that life on the communal farms is
primitive. It is equally true, however, that famines and plagues which formerly
took millions of lives are now unknown. The Chinese farmer is extremely
poor, certainly. The conditions under which he lives have been improved a
little, but only a very little and that very slowly." (*La Chine et son ombre*, p. 203.)

life which is in no way like that of the masses in India and in China. There is little more that can be done in Japan to improve farming techniques or effect land reclamation. The country must look to the expansion of its industry for the solution of its feeding problem.

Indonesia has a population of 87,000,000. It also has to face difficulties of food supply for its still backward people. These are concentrated largely on the islands of Java and Madura which have an area one-third that of France. In Sumatra there are 1,080 persons to the square mile, whereas in Borneo there are only 18 and scarcely more in Celebes and the Moluccas. One of the keys to the problem here could be transfers of population, but that is always difficult and costly. Government plans provide for migration from the densely peopled zones to the enormous areas which have yet to be exploited.

Apart from Asia, the other precariously balanced parts of the world are Egypt, North Africa and Central America. Egypt has to provide for a population of 25,000,000, which increases by 2·4 per cent a year and is concentrated in 3·8 per cent of the country's territory at a density verging on 1,400 people to the square mile. Half the population is under twenty years of age. It is possible to increase the cultivated area by draining the 1,750,000 acres of lagoons in the Nile delta and, even more, by enlarging the irrigated area by means of the Aswan dam. Crop yields could also be improved. But it is principally to intensified industrialization that Egypt must look to provide for its people and raise their very low standard of life.

It is to this end that the Constantine plan in Algeria is directed. It is necessary, there, to provide work for a population which is expected to double in twenty-five years.[13] "The Algerian revolt", writes A. Sauvey, "is the fruit of the pressure of population. A workless peasant is only too ready to seize the rifle that will get him food: while the briefless lawyer is the essential revolutionary agent."

In the Caribbean area, the little islands in the Antilles support a dense population—nowhere less than 350 to the square mile— at a very low standard of life. The most thickly populated island is Barbados, with 1,360 persons to the square mile. If we

[13] Cf. J. -L. Fyot, "Développement économique de l'Algérie et cohabitation" in *Revue de l'action Populaire*, Nov. 1960.

except Jamaica, Trinidad and Tobago, which have some oil and mineral resources, the principal sources of wealth for the greater part of these territories are farming and fishing. The efficiencies of these could be considerably increased. The same can be said of Salvador, Guatemala, Honduras and Costa Rica.

We can look to Holland and Japan for examples of what can be done for agriculture in densely populated countries. Holland is one of the most densely populated countries in the world, with 875 persons to the square mile, a density four times greater than that of France. The Dutch are, however, an ingenious and industrious people who have learned how to put every square inch of ground to good use. By strenuous efforts, part of its territory has been recovered from the sea. Its farmers are taught their craft in 261 agricultural and 121 horticultural colleges, to say nothing of 1,622 continuation classes attended by young farmers. The soil is poor in many parts, but it is exploited intensively. Between Rotterdam and the Hague, where crops are grown under glass and in hot-houses, ground is not sold by the hectare (about $2\frac{1}{2}$ acres), but is parcelled out by the square metre. Thanks to this intensive cultivation, Holland not only feeds its own people, but is also able to export some 40 per cent of its produce.

In Japan, where the pressure of population is equally great, methods of cultivation are rather those of the market gardener than of the farmer. By using modern techniques and advanced irrigation systems, yields are obtained which are six times greater than those of India.

Side by side with over-populated areas, in which, moreover, there still exist more or less considerable opportunities for progress, there are to be found enormous areas possessing very great potentialities.

At the present time, only some 9 to 10 per cent of the land surface of the globe is cultivated: that is, some 5,000,000 square miles. Some 17 per cent is meadow and pasture and 29 per cent forest and woodland. Almost half the land surface (43·5 per cent) is unproductive, consisting of mountains, fallow land, and built up areas.

B. R. Sen, the director-general of F.A.O., has given us some information on this subject:

C.H.—3

It is often thought that the milliard hectares which is cultivated today, about ten per cent of the land surface of the globe, is all that is in fact cultivable. This is far from being the case. It is only in the temperate regions of the northern hemisphere and the tropical parts of Asia where one can truthfully say that the cultivable areas are fully utilized. It is still disputed whether there is a possibility of cultivating the vast areas of humid tropical forest around the equator, mainly in Africa and Latin America. Nevertheless, as Dr. Kellog, a great American authority on soil problems, has demonstrated, if we brought into use only 20 per cent of the unused area of the tropical zone, we would add 1,000,000,000 acres, or 40 per cent, to the world's cultivated land.

In those parts of Asia which are densely populated, there is little possibility of extending the cultivated area; but where-ever irrigation is possible, and it is, for the most part, in the valley lands where most of the people live, men should be able to harvest two or three crops a year where now there is usually only one. A recent enquiry by F.A.O. for example, has shown that in the basin of the lower Ganges or Brahmaputra, where there are 130,000,000 people, the cultivated area could be doubled in the space of a year, if full use were made of the water which is now allowed to flow away almost unutilized. Apart from this, there are possibilities of increasing crop yields.

There are also considerable possibilities for extending the cultivated areas in the well-watered regions of the southern hemisphere temperate zone. Such areas are to be found in southern Australia, Uruguay and southern Brazil. It has been estimated that in the south of Australia alone, 160,000,000 acres of well-watered and reasonably level land could be brought under cultivation, instead of 40,000,000 as at present. It is also probable that there are large reserves of land beyond the present northern limit of the cultivable zone, principally in Canada and Russia, which will one day be usable.[14]

It is true that the possibilities which are now open to pioneers who wish to establish themselves on unutilized land are few. This is because, in most cases, preliminary works are called for which are beyond the compass of individual means. According to F.A.O.: "it is not possible to open up to the plough large

[14] Speaking at Rome (22 Jan. 1959) to the Societa italiana per l'Organizzazione Internazionale.

areas of the new lands except after concerted governmental efforts calling for massive investment and, in some cases, considerable research. In the long run, however, there are certain considerable opportunities for extending the area of cultivation."[15]

As things are, one of the greatest obstacles is finance. The cost of the economic base necessary for the large-scale activities required to bring into cultivation a whole region or river basin would be very large.

In former times, some of the lands which today are desert or semi-desert were major sources of cereals. There is nothing in principle to prevent the course of history from being reversed. With the means at our disposal today we could rescue the formerly cultivated lands along the Nile, the Indus, the Tigris and the Euphrates.

There are parts of the U.S.A. and of the temperate zone of South America which are well watered and only partially utilized, due to bad communications and insufficient pressure of population. Thus, in Argentina only 20 per cent of the cultivable area is in fact cultivated. In Brazil the proportion is only 11 per cent, in Peru 10 per cent, and in Colombia 8 per cent. It is well known that in Brazil the native farmer neglects his land because there is no convenient market for his produce, nor roads or railways to carry it to the great centres of population. A visitor to one of these under-cultivated areas spoke to a peasant whom he met: "Well, my poor friend, is your land so bad, then, that it will grow nothing?" "Oh!", was the reply, "If we planted, the crop would grow." Isolated and lost, almost, in the vastness of nature as they are, why should the people of the Brazilian bush grow crops in excess of their own and their families' needs?[16]

In the light of all this, it appears that the true problem which faces men today is less one of over-population than of under-development.

To advocate, as some people do, a limitation of births as a necessary preliminary to any action aimed at improving human

[15] F.A.O., *Agriculture in the World Economy*, p. 37.

[16] The unused land in South America alone would permit an increase in the cultivated area of about 900,000,000 acres. This is nearly one-eighth of the present arable and pasture land in the world.

nutrition, is to ignore the considerable possibilities which exist in many parts of the world. It is true, nevertheless, that prompt action by appropriate means and on the required scale is necessary, if economic development is not to lag behind the growth of population. The capital resources and advanced techniques of western countries ought to be used, as we have argued elsewhere,[17] to help to keep the under-developed countries in balance during the difficult time of growth.

Doubtless, a time will come when the developing countries, in their full vigour, will look to the example of the more developed lands and will understand for themselves the need to bring population growth under control. "The experience of the technically well equipped countries with a steady rate of economic and cultural development seems to show that the pressure of population on the means of subsistence is reduced by a twofold change: there is not only a rapid growth of outputs, but also a natural reduction in the birth rate to a moderate level, at which it tends to be stabilized."[18] Experience does seem to show that when a people enjoys a better standard of life—as regards food, housing, sanitation and medical care—it is the death rate which falls at first: the birth rate falls, in its turn, only when the greater part of the population have reached a more advanced standard of civilization, in which reflection and a collective conscience come to play an important part.[19]

On this matter, the position of the Catholic Church is perfectly clear. It is not opposed to the regulation of births which, indeed, in certain conditions seems to it to be desirable. It raises no objection to the method of birth regulation known as the "safe period", holding the use of this method to be legitimate when there are good grounds for regulating or spacing births. But it condemns, as unnatural and degrading, the various types of contraception which deny the natural order and make hedonism the rule of morality.

[17] Cf. *Pays sous-développés et Coopération technique.*

[18] Statement of the Malines Union for Social Studies, June 1954.

[19] Although it is denied by some, there does seem to be a connection between living standards and birth rate, countries with more advanced civilizations being less prolific than are poor countries. In the latter, there are practically no checks on natural fertility. This explains the rapid growth of population in the under-developed countries during the first stage of their development.

We are aware that these arguments will seem to be unconvincing and of doubtful value in face of the urgency of the problems caused by the growth of population in already densely populated countries. We can answer by asking whether the advocates of birth control might not themselves be mistaken in their reckoning. Progress in agricultural science and technique is far from ended. In this sphere, the future undoubtedly holds for us more than one surprise.

There are further objections. It is not possible for us to ignore the grave dangers that would flow from a methodically organized campaign for contraception, dangers both for man and for society. There would be a rapid ageing of the population, with all that this entails; a perversion of love and of sexuality; a dangerous blow to the maternal instinct, so that the coming of a child might cease to look like a happy event; to say nothing of psychological, religious and moral shocks consequent on a harsh break from a former mental balance. The unsoundness of a contraceptive civilization has been well expressed by S. de Lestapis:

> The erotic civilization of contraception by devaluing fatherhood and motherhood is more responsible than is generally believed for the state of confusion between the sexes so characteristic of the contemporary world and so prejudicial—as all child psychologists agree—to the sound education of children.[20]

In the last place, it must be said against those who see in "birth control" a means of combating abortion, that the number of abortions has not only not diminished but has increased in countries which have adopted birth control. A culture which accepts contraception turns its back on the act of creation and finds itself ready to adopt abortion, too.

[20] S. de Lestapis, *Family Planning and Modern Problems* (Burns Oates, 1961), p. 87.

III

THE GEOGRAPHY OF HUNGER

ONE fact leaps at once to the eye when one looks at a map showing the regions in which malnutrition is, as it were, the rule. All the hungry lands are to be found in the tropical and sub-tropical zones.

These lands, usually under-developed, suffer under a climate which makes life and civilization more difficult than in the temperate regions. Soil very quickly loses its quality in the great heat of the sun or under the downpour of torrential rains. Capriciousness of the seasons and long periods of drought, allied to the cultural methods employed and other unfavourable human factors, are to a large extent responsible for the prevalence of low crop yields.

From this it is easier to understand the present differences between the nutritional standards of the various parts of the globe. It should be added that in the hungry lands the medical situation and the rate of morbidity are such as to make a large number of men incapable of truly productive work.[1]

Some writers hold the view that the astonishing development of western civilization is due to a large extent to the advantage of a temperate climate. This is the opinion of Huntington in particular, who points to the decline of the eastern civilizations to become today, to use his expression, "cradles of famine and the deepest poverty".

On the other hand, other peoples have not only prospered on lands which are apparently very much poorer, but have also spread out into other continents and built civilizations which have conquered the modern world. All this has come

---

[1] "Even to this day, 200,000,000 people in India suffer from malaria. Many of them can do little more than vegetate. To provide treatment for these invalids is to do more than a work of humanity; it is also to furnish the community with producers where formerly there were only consumers." (Dr Pierre Theil, *Pour que les hommes vivent mieux*, p. 65.)

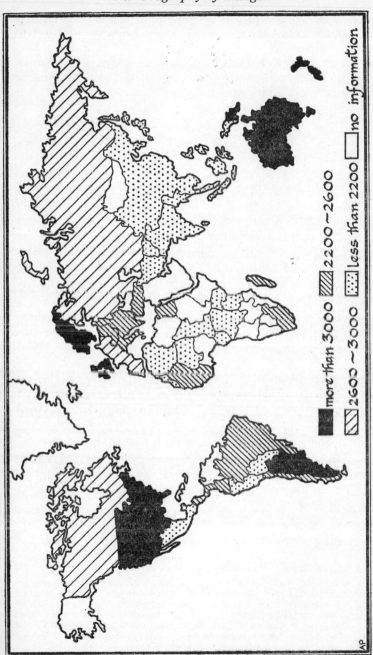

SUPPLY OF CALORIES PER PERSON PER DAY

about as though the so-called temperate regions conferred on their inhabitants—provided that they understood how to protect themselves against extremes of temperature—a vitality, an energy, a spirit of enterprise, a dynamism which would seem to become atrophied in much easier and, above all, less variable climates.[2]

The main areas of defective nutrition, whether in quality or quantity, are in India, a large part of the Far East, in vast regions of South and Central America, in Africa and in the Near East.[3]

We can distinguish three types of diet. There is an advanced diet, based on sugar, fat and animal products. This is typical of northern America and western Europe. Then there are areas where the diet is based on cereals and where animal products are little used. This is the diet of China and of some countries in the Far and Middle East. On the bottom rung are the primitive diets, where the calories consumed are deficient both in quality and quantity. This is typical of some equatorial regions where cassava and mealy plantains form the basic diet. It is in these regions, where the diets are unbalanced, that the diseases due to malnutrition are found most commonly and in their gravest forms.

The level of nutrition in the Far East is among the lowest known. The individual intake of calories in south-east Asia is not even as much as two-thirds of that in the more developed countries of Europe.

In India, the typical intake is less than half that in Australia, New Zealand, Argentina and U.S.A. Except in Pakistan, where it is about a quarter of that of France and a sixth of that of Australia and New Zealand, the consumption of animal protein is almost negligible.

People in the Far East are almost entirely vegetarian, eating cereals (mainly rice), tubers and dried legumes such as haricot

[2] Ellsworth Huntington, *Civilization and Climate.*

[3] Mention must be made of the difficulty of the problem and of the unreality of certain general statements or statistics referring to the whole world, of which use is sometimes made. The map of the hungry must be drawn country by country, even district by district. It happens frequently that in moving from one area to another of the same country we meet considerable variations in standards of nutrition. Hence comes the necessity (as we shall see later) of multiplying enquiries into the subject. (See ch. 5 below.)

and soya beans and peas. It is these last that provide the indispensable proteins and some fat. Milk, butter and cheese are almost unknown in China and Japan. There is no stock rearing and so meat is scarce. In the Chinese countryside pork and chicken are eaten only on festival days.

India has more cattle than anywhere else in the world and yet is vegetarian because of a ban on slaughter, the cow being a sacred animal. Only the milk is used, and the yields of that are low. Poor feeding allows of an annual average yield per cow of about 40 gallons. In Holland, the yield is 790 gallons, and in U.S.A., 495 gallons.

Fish forms part of the diet of people living near rivers or the sea; but except for Japan, where the fisheries are equipped on an industrial scale, the means are usually lacking that would permit a more intensive exploitation of fish resources.[4] There is no way of transporting the fish to distant centres and the fishing boats are primitive. These facts have so far stood in the way of growth in this industry, by which much could be done to improve the protein content of the diet.

In most of the countries of South-east Asia, food supplies, home produced and imported together, are not enough to provide a satisfactory diet. Critical shortages have become rare, but diets are still qualitatively defective. They do not possess in the right proportions all the nutritional elements of which the human being has need.

Java and Madura, in the Indonesian archipelago, are also lands of chronic under-nourishment. They have to feed a population larger than that of Great Britain on an area smaller than that of Greece. Their rubber and copra outputs are not enough to buy them a balanced diet. Sugar, fats, meat and milk together provide only 8 per cent of the calories consumed, while rice provides 50 per cent, starchy foods 25 per cent and maize 8 per cent, with all the consequences for health of such a diet.

At the present time, it seems that nobody dies of hunger in China. Can the same be said of India? Those who have travelled

---

[4] The Japanese fisheries are among the most important in the world. It is true that the Japanese people eat less meat than do others in the Far East, but on the other hand, they eat a lot of fish. Shell-fish and edible algae are eaten in great quantities: indeed, they eat more algae than they do meat. (Cf. Pierre Gourou, *La Terre et l'Homme en Extrême-Orient.*)

over this immense land during the last few years have found themselves haunted by poverty. Tibor Mende, quoting from Pierre and Renée Gosset's *Terrifiante Asie*, has this to say: "One hundred million villagers have never had enough to eat. . . . Investigators will tell you that the Indian people are under-nourished. But that has been their condition for ten or twenty generations, since long before there were any investigators. The Indian's bone formation and his very shape have been modified, thinned and made weaker. Hence the disquieting grace of these slim figures, with breadth neither of shoulders nor of hips. One could swear that the enormous eyes, admirable in themselves, have eaten up the thin faces." These faces of hungry women and children are with you everywhere, in the countryside as well as in the great cities such as Bombay and, above all, Calcutta.

One can understand the remark of an Indian to a European who was staying in the country: "For us Asiatics, the most important thing is not to be free, but to eat regularly."

Latin America is the continent which perhaps abounds most in contrasts, given its diversity of climates, agricultural produce and peoples.

Argentina and Uruguay are important producers of meat and their levels of nutrition are relatively high, when compared to those of most countries in Europe. But alongside them live peoples condemned to a famine diet. The Indians of the high plateaux of the Andes, who feed mainly on maize and potatoes, are not unique. The countryman in the interior of Brazil lives principally on starchy foods—cassava or plantains in some districts—on maize or rice, haricot beans, sometimes some sugar, with small quantities of meat or dried fish. The agricultural workers in the West Indies live on rice, beans and salted cod. This monotonous diet, in which eggs and milk rarely figure, is deficient in protein, in fresh vegetables and in fruit. Hence the high frequency of deficiency diseases which is found in these regions, particularly among dwellers in the Amazon basin.

On Brazil, Josué de Castro writes: "Biological and chemical analysis of diets in the Amazon basin show innumerable nutrition deficiencies. Their insufficiency leaps to the eye, by reason of the tiny quantity, or even complete absence, of

FOOD PRODUCTION IN LATIN AMERICA

certain protective foods—meat, milk, cheese, butter, eggs, vegetables and fruits. In addition, the smallness of the diet is striking. Feeding is poor, insufficient and incredibly dull. The entire consumption of a whole day for one of these people would not be enough for one meal for an inhabitant of another climatic region."[5]

In the single-crop areas of Brazil, such as the sugar zone in the north-east and the cocoa state of Bahia, where the large estate is typical, the landless labourers are very poor and chronically under-fed. In other parts of the north-east the food situation is generally better, but there the major scourge is periodic drought, which sometimes forces the entire population out on the roads in search of something to eat. Their small reserves exhausted, the people are reduced to eating roots, wild oats and tree bark.

From the nutritional point of view, Colombia and Peru are not much better than many countries of the Far East. They have dangerous deficiencies, as also have some of the Central American countries and Caribbean islands: Honduras, San Salvador, Mexico, the Federation of the West Indies.

Dr Masseyeff notes that in hungry lands there is often a connection between under-nourishment and the use of stimulants: coco leaves, tea, betel nut, hashish, opium, etc. "One of the reasons for their use may be a desire to deceive hunger. The drugs which are as commonly used in Asia as in South America, and even in Africa, become as much a necessity almost as food. Large areas are devoted to their cultivation."[6]

The somewhat better standards of the Middle East do not appear to have been much improved of recent years. In some places they have probably become worse because of the increasing population on the cultivable lands and the rise in prices.

The nomads, who are still numerous in this region where so much is desert, live mainly on cereals, dates, milk and milk products. The settled cultivators have a diet containing less milk products and composed principally of cereals and fruits. In both cases, meat generally forms only a small part of the food supply.

[5] Josué de Castro, *Hunger in Brazil*, p. 57.
[6] R. Masseyeff, *Hunger*, p. 57.

In the fertile parts of Syria and Iraq, where there are often 100 to 120 persons to the square mile, food supplies are poor and the daily intake of calories is rarely as high as 2,000. Meat is served only on festive days, but large amounts of olives, figs and various fruits are available.

The situation in the arid lands of the immense plateau of Saudi Arabia, in Iran and the Yemen is not much better: in these regions under-nourishment is chronic. Only the oil-

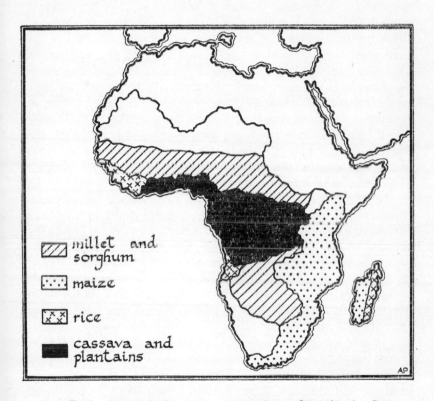

millet and sorghum

maize

rice

cassava and plantains

BASIC FOODS IN AFRICA SOUTH OF THE SAHARA

bearing states of the Persian Gulf escape the universal poverty of the East.

Improvement of nutrition in these parts is partly tied up with the possibilities of putting arid and semi-arid lands to use. Of this we shall be speaking later.

Although standards of nutrition have been raised since the Cameroons Conference in 1949, Africa remains an under-fed continent. The information available to us indicates that in Central and tropical Africa the average daily intake of calories is now 2,250, whereas it was 2,100 in 1949. This is almost enough for estimated needs in these regions; but the value of the ingredients of the diet leaves much to be desired.

In many of the villages to the south of the Sahara there is also a periodical time of shortage. Reserves of millet and rice are generally exhausted just at the time when agricultural work on a large scale begins again, towards the end of the dry season. At such times, it is common for the daily intake to fall below two-thirds of what is required. This shortage persists until the harvest. Meanwhile, the people eat whatever they can find: field-mice, locusts, wild fruits and seeds. Leaves of the baobab and other trees are dried and ground to powder to serve for food.

The main constituent of the diet varies with the climatic zone. In the areas bordering on the Sahara and the Kalahari, sorghum and millet, which are better adapted to the dry climate, furnish about three-quarters of the calories. The principal dish consists of a paste of millet or sorghum soaked in a sauce or dressing, accompanied sometimes by ground-nuts, rice or peas. During the dry season, which lasts for from five to seven months, fruits and vegetables are scarce, as also are milk and meat. Dried fish is on sale in most African markets and is used on a large scale.

In a large part of the savannah region of East and Central Africa, maize has more or less replaced millet as the main item of diet. Rainfall is more abundant in these regions and the cultivation of starchy foods is of importance. Maize pan-cakes and edible roots are eaten with a fermented sauce, made from beans, peppers and leaves of the baobab tree. Closer to the equatorial zone, with its dense and humid forests, the cultivation of yams and cassava with plantains becomes dominant. Because of the tsetse fly in this region, cattle rearing is almost impossible and in consequence the intake of animal protein is small.[7]

The diet of pastoral tribes is based on cattle rearing and so is ordinarily richer in animal protein. It consists of curdled milk mixed with blood, to which is nowadays added cereals obtained from neighbouring agricultural tribes in exchange for meat and milk. It is the fishermen of the coasts and lakes who enjoy the highest protein intake of all native Africans.

The feeding of the indigenous working population in the rapidly growing African towns is generally wanting in both quality and quantity. In most cases, 80 to 90 per cent of the children are under-fed.

With their traditional, unprogressive and relatively unproductive methods of agriculture, the countries of North Africa—Morocco, Algeria, Tunisia—have great difficulty in providing for their rapidly growing populations. On the other hand, the more favourable climate in Southern Africa does much to make the situation there less precarious.

Conditions of soil and climate do not of themselves explain the state of under-production and of general under-nourishment that are found in backward countries. There are other factors involved, social, psychological and religious, which often make an already difficult situation more so.

The country dwellers in the under-developed lands of Africa, Latin American and Asia are still for the most part illiterate. The people of more remote villages in many parts have been given neither instruction nor advice on how they might change the traditional methods which cannot provide the increased production necessary.

In India, as in many other Eastern countries, the scythe is almost unknown and the crop is still harvested, much more slowly and laboriously, with the sickle. Oxen even tread out the grain, as in biblical times, and the grain is still thrown into the air to be winnowed by the wind. Use of fertilizer and selected

---

[7] In certain under-developed countries, and particularly in Africa, hunting is often a means of procuring extra protein. The hunters are not particular as to what they hunt: everything is good to them, snakes, rodents, birds, carnivores. But this often brings serious risks to health: "As a result of autopsies on people who have eaten lion and snake flesh, Pales has found the origin of parasitism by *Porocephalus armillatus*. Rat hunting brings a useful addition of protein both in Africa and in Asia, but it is also a cause of endemic disease." (Lengelle, *Le Tiers-Monde*, p. 217.)

seed is still unknown to the vast majority. Because the Indian
and the Arab use very little manure, the land becomes progressively poorer, a process which nobody thinks of halting by the
process of green manuring. In India, the dung is dried and used
for fuel: elsewhere, where cattle are few, it is difficult to renew
the humus in the soil and deterioration goes on.

Attempts to change the peoples' farming techniques often
come up against a force of inertia which is difficult to over-
come. Until quite recently, the people in the Tanala country,
in the high plateau of Madagascar, maintained themselves on
rice grown on plots of ground in the mountains, which had
been cleared by burning and were not very fertile, and on
whatever they could gather in the forest. Today, these people,
organized by the agricultural service, must cultivate the flooded
low lands, where they can get five times the yield of rice, but
also have to work harder. The work does not please them and
they go about their task sluggishly, looking back with regret
upon the time when all they had to do to prepare a seed-bed
was to set fire to some grass. As soon as the administration
relaxes its vigilance, back they go to the old method. Why should
they do otherwise? Needs and living standards are as simple as
could be and they do not as yet feel the desire for anything else.
In former times, the Malagasy lived meanly, it is true, but he did
not have to work as hard as he must now. If sleeping energies
are to be brought to action, a powerful "mystique" is needed.

Some people think that the famous "island lassitude",
described by travellers in former times, is more often than
not a symptom of a chronic state of malnutrition. The work-
man is simply unable to put forth a prolonged effort. Anyway,
most of these people live in a subsistence economy, far away
from the great centres, and they have nothing to stimulate them
to change their ways of life.

The nomadic or semi-nomadic peoples of the desert regions
of the East offer us a typical example of this. The labour of
the peasant is repugnant to the nomad, accustomed to his life
of relative idleness in the midst of his flocks. Furthermore, a
sedentary life is incompatible with his wandering habits. As
G. W. Murray says, "The Arab is perfectly happy to pass the
whole day smoking, gossiping and drinking coffee. His only
work is the rearing of camels. All the rest he leaves to the

women: setting-up of tents, caring for the sheep and goats, attending to water-supplies."

The indolence of the pastoral nomad, roaming the deserts from water hole to water hole and from pasturage to pasturage, is legendary. He prefers the discomfort of camping and striking camp to the manual labour of the peasant, which, indeed, appears to the Bedouin of Sinai as a degradation, as C. J. Jarvis has observed with some humour. "Suggest to an Arab that he dig a ditch to his camp and you will see him put on the look of a martyr. Take your eyes off him for a moment and he will, more likely than not, take his family and himself off to Palestine and stay there for a year or so, so as to escape having to do some work."

It can be understood that the policy of integrating these wandering tribes which is now being followed in the Middle East is not going to be easy to carry out.[8] To be brought to a successful conclusion, the policy must put into operation a series of measures designed to settle the people on a portion of territory and equip them to work it. This would include digging wells, furnishing tools, establishing schools, etc. Often, it will be found necessary to have a period of semi-nomadic life, during which the Bedouin can spend part of the year in agricultural pursuits and part on their wanderings. After preparing the soil and sowing the seed (the seed being generally provided free by the government), they can wander away for several months with their flocks and then come back for the harvest.

In many of the under-developed lands there are strong forces of tradition and religious interdicts which put powerful obstacles in the way of modern agricultural techniques and higher nutritional standards. This is not true of India only: it is found also in the Philippines, in Africa and among the small tribes of Latin America which are as yet largely untouched by Western civilization.

In Africa, many people are animists. Their religion exerts a powerful influence on their social and economic affairs, with numerous interdicts, some temporary, others permanent, some affecting the whole people, some only isolated individuals. These taboos, which are connected with the practice of fetishism,

---

[8] Cf. Mohamed Awad, "The settlement of nomadic and semi-nomadic tribes in the Middle East," *International Labour Review*, Jan. 1959.

can affect foodstuffs or methods of preparing the food. In parts of Togoland, for example, there are taboos on the eating of buffalo meat, cheetah, dog, cat or crocodile. Those who go to the witch-doctor to ask him to turn misfortune from them (whether it be in the form of sickness, or sterility, or the deaths of children), can expect to be forbidden to partake, for a long or short time, of a list of foods, such as game, fish, bean cakes, palm oil, etc.

Often these taboos name protective foods, rich in protein. Thus, in certain parts of Tanganyika women are forbidden to drink milk, while in Uganda it is to men that this prohibition applies. In several regions, eggs are taboo for women.

It is in India, unquestionably, that taboos on foodstuffs have the gravest consequences for the nutrition of a whole people. As we have already said, India has the largest number of cattle in the world, estimated at 190,000,000 head, or one beast for every two inhabitants. At least one-third of these are thought to be not worth keeping and all are of little use: yet their slaughter is forbidden. Their main use is as a source of energy: they pull carts and draw water and their droppings are used for fuel and, in building, for plastering of walls and floors. (These last are very expensive uses in other ways.) This herd takes up for food four times the total land revenue of India, according to A. Guerrin.

To make matters worse, religious custom will not allow war to be waged on the main enemies of the farmer, monkeys and rats. The monkeys go about in swarms and do great damage, yet no man lifts a hand against them from fear of bringing down upon himself the anger of the monkey-god Hanuman. They can sometimes be seen even stealing the seed in the footsteps of the sower. As for the rats, it is only secretly that one can try to be rid of them. M. André Philip reported on his return from a visit of investigation to India: "The Indian Government has tried to take action against the rats. I have seen a village where traps were set for them. But when the rats were taken, they were put into a sack, carried to the lands of the next village, and emptied out there: for it is not lawful to kill any living thing."[9]

[9] A. Philip, "Les données du problème agricole au Japon et aux Indes", a speech given under the auspices of the Assemblée des Présidents de Chambres d'Agriculture, Paris, 1960.

The Hindu belief in the oneness of life and the reincarnation of souls in other beings, whether of men or animals, makes every living thing sacred and not to be killed. This brings unexpected consequences nowadays, as M. Philip notes, with some little malice, after having drawn attention to a degree of change which is now taking place:

"I have to say that in this respect I have noticed a certain change since my last visit thirty years ago. Not in Calcutta, alas! There, when one walks through the city, one sees the cows on what corresponds to the avenue de l'Opéra, camped on the pavement, abandoned and dying of hunger. While it is forbidden to kill, nobody is bound to keep them alive. In Bombay, on the other hand, all the cows have been rounded up and installed in a modern agricultural centre. There they are fed adequately and supply one-third of all the milk drunk in the city of Bombay. At the same time and perhaps somewhat pharisaically (although a little hypocrisy is sometimes the beginning of virtue), the cows which do not give milk are sold to the Australians. They are not killed. Of course, nobody knows what the Australians do with them. Perhaps they have homes for tired cows; or perhaps, the cows end up in tins of corned beef and are exported to every corner of the world. One prefers not to know."

The pressure of population which drives the Japanese or Chinese peasant to give every care to his land does not appear to be a sufficient incentive when a sort of religious fatalism infects a whole people, making it more ready for passive resignation than for battle against the elements.

But perhaps even more serious are the effects of having agrarian institutions ill-adapted to the conditions of modern farm production. It is difficult to obtain satisfactory results where plots are too small or are heavily mortgaged, and so long as no attempt is made to reform institutions or change the existing state of affairs.

In numerous countries where the economy is basically agrarian, it is the view of authorities that one of the major difficulties in the way of economic development and the betterment of living conditions lies in that direction. An excessive parcelling out of farms, sometimes alongside *latifundia* which are put to insufficient use; a form of tenure which is

disadvantageous to the farmer; farm tenancies or share crop-
ping agreements which take excessive shares; all these are so
many obstacles in the way of productive investments.

It has been calculated that in the most densely populated
countries, such as India, Ceylon, Egypt, Korea, Indonesia and
Haiti, the cultivable land is less than five-sixths of an acre per
inhabitant. Most of the farms are very small and scarcely
provide enough for the maintenance of the farmer and his
family.

In most of the Indian provinces, where the great number of
unprofitable farms pose a difficult problem, the average extent
of these small plots is between four and five acres.

It is estimated that in the Indies the minimum for a profitable
farm ought to be two hectares (five acres), of which 0·92
hectares ought to be well watered. But in India only about a
third of the land under cultivation is sufficiently watered,
normally, either by rainfall or by irrigation. Each farm, then,
has on average scarcely two acres of well-watered land. For
such a farm to become profitable there would have to be
added 1·6 hectares (four acres) of unirrigated land.[10]

One can see from this the peculiarly difficult problem which
its farm structure poses for that country.

In the Philippines, the pressure of population is less apparent
and the mean area of the farms there is 10 acres. But because
of a very uneven division of land-holdings and the concentration
of the population on Luzon and in the Viscayas islands, more
than half of the farms are of less than 5 acres.

In South America, there is as a rule no lack of land. The
agrarian problem there is the co-existence of very large estates,
which are under-utilized, with quite tiny farms which are not
capable normally of supporting a farm family.

The *latifundia* are characteristic of the land-owning system
of Latin America. Throughout the continent—except for
some districts in Costa Rica, Haiti, Mexico and Salvador—
most of the cultivable land belongs to great landowners. In
the whole of Latin America, about 1·5 per cent of the landed
properties are of more than 6,000 hectares (15,000 acres) and
occupy, in all, about half of all the agricultural land. For the

[10] U.N.: *Agrarian Reform: structural defects which hamper economic development* (1951), p. 8.

most part these lands are not farmed intensively. They contain a great part of the land which has lain fallow, and in the same hands, for generations. There are vast plantations on these *latifundia*, but the greater part of the estates are not used. At the other end of the scale there are tiny holdings where agriculture of a small-holding nature is practised on bits of poor and worn-out land. It is true that there are some farmers with moderate holdings, but it is the small farmers and the landless labourers who form the great mass of the rural population.[11]

As regards the South American countries, there is an additional consideration. Relations between land-owners and farmers or share-croppers are often enough badly defined and not subject to precise rules, an arrangement which works to the disadvantage of the weaker parties. In the Indian countryside, it is the zemindars and usurers who are rife, taking the best part of the peasants' income. Indeed, the Indian farmer is in debt for the whole of his life. Such agrarian systems cannot fail to have their effects on agricultural outputs.

In Venezuela and Colombia, in the teeth of all that is logical, there is land on the mountain sides which would best be used for pasture and forestry, but which is cultivated intensively to provide for the needs of the farmers themselves. At the same time the valley lands, much more suitable for their labours, are used for pasture. A report of the I.B.R.D. (International Bank for Reconstruction and Development) has pointed to this anomalous situation and to the dangers which could flow from such a use of land.

A large number of farm families are trying to live on tiny parcels of land, sited often on slopes of some 25 or even 45 degrees or more. This type of farming is devastating in its effects on the land, aggravating erosion and creating other difficulties. Even so, it is not possible for people to live decently. This form of land use is one of the most important causes of the small output of farm labour and of the poverty which is widespread in the rural areas.[12]

The conclusion to which we are led by our analysis of these different factors is that the problem of under-nourishment

[11] U.N.: *Agrarian Reform: structural defects which hamper economic development* (1951), p. 21.
[12] Ibid., p. 22.

must be tackled from several quarters at the same time. The elements of the problem are more complex than appears at first sight. Solutions are not only of a technical or financial nature. It would be foolish to hope for a correct solution of so vital a problem without the joint application of measures looking to a better distribution of land, wider knowledge of good agricultural techniques and a great educational effort on behalf of the mass of the people.

IV

MALNUTRITION

NUTRITIONAL deficiencies, or malnutrition, are widespread and often serious. A badly balanced diet which is too poor in certain elements called protective—essentially proteins, vitamins and mineral salts—can show itself to be more harmful than mere under-nourishment, an insufficient intake of food which is otherwise sufficiently varied.

It could be said that malnutrition due to a lack of proteins or vitamins is a greater scourge than cancer or tuberculosis. Often it is the cause of the high rate of infantile mortality which is seen in under-developed countries, and it is found at the base of the stunted growth of both children and adults. Certain ills, better diagnosed nowadays, are endemic in poor countries. Such are kwashiorkor, beriberi, pellagra and numerous eye troubles, all of them consequences of a diet which is deficient in one or other of the elements which are essential to health.

Authorities on nutritional questions have noted the ravages caused by unbalanced diets in regions such as Africa and South and Central America and bend their energies to struggle not only against hunger in the ordinary sense of the word, but also against various forms of malnutrition, to which the term "specific hunger" has been applied.

Investigations have been carried on now for some years and all point to the close connection which exists between diet and general health. "Our biological condition", writes H. C. Sherman, "depends to a degree greater than we think on our habitual diet. The influence of feeding on health and, consequently, on balanced physiological development, begins before we are born. Nutrition affects both the growth and the mental development of children and adolescents and, therefore, the efficiency and expectation of life of adults."[1]

[1] Quoted in the F.A.O. Handbook, *Feeding in School*, p. 30.

An ill-nourished and weak organism is open to invasion from various pathogenic agents against which it is in no state to fight. It has been shown again and again that dietary deficiencies are particularly apt to weaken resistance against diseases borne by microbes: tuberculosis, and various eye diseases, for example. It is among people who are underfed and deficient in vitamins that infections from microbes and parasites break out and develop most vigorously. The epidemic of Spanish influenza in 1918 was so violent only because it fell upon a population undermined by the privations of war. It is not to be wondered at that it is in the under-developed countries, where the diet leaves much to be desired, that outbreaks which decimate the population are most often seen.

An important factor in the morbidity and mortality of large sections of the populations of Africa, Latin America and Asia is the prevalent deficiency of proteins. In the report presented in 1956 by the committee of experts for South and East Asia it is noted that doctors, who are often ignorant of the effects of malnutrition, do not pay attention to the minor troubles it causes in women who are pregnant or are breast-feeding, nor recognize the causes of upsets in the development of children below the age of school entry. The report concludes:

> Protein deficiency is perhaps one of the most important causes of a high rate of premature and still births. Similarly, a high mortality rate from congenital debility during the first year of life is possibly indicative of a protein deficiency, since the number of deaths from this cause is very small in a population which is healthy and well fed.

Much has been done of late years to throw light on this problem. Particularly important research has been done into the need for amino acids of certain age groups (children, adolescents, etc.). Most valuable results have been obtained, showing the amino acid content of various foods, which enable us to discover the incidence of malnutrition and of diseases due to a deficiency of proteins. This fundamental research, the importance of which is now admitted on all sides, has also demonstrated the indispensability of supplementing diets which are deficient with sufficient protein of good quality,

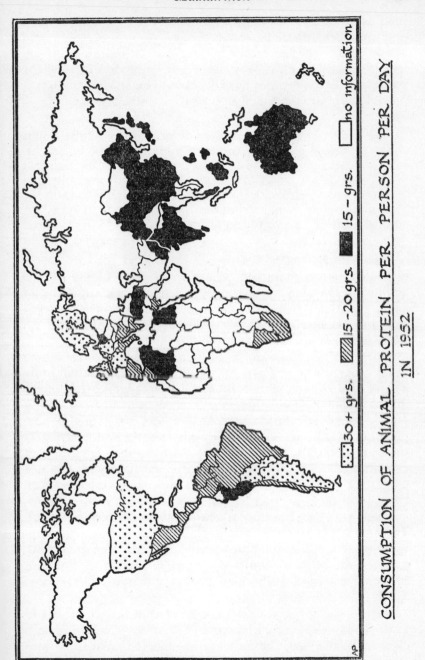

CONSUMPTION OF ANIMAL PROTEIN PER PERSON PER DAY IN 1952

such as is found in liquid or powdered milk, in eggs, and in other products of animal origin.

The results of this research have been condensed in the report of the F.A.O. on *Protein Needs*, published in 1958 for specialists. While it is not possible here to enter into detail, it is possible to quote the conclusion reached in the report:

> In practice, the consumption of protein by adults ought not go below one gram for each kilogram of body weight. The protein ought to be of different sorts and it is desirable that part of it be of animal origin. For the growing body and in pregnancy and while breast-feeding a certain quantity of animal protein is indispensable. During growth it ought to form a major part of the total protein intake.

For children under six months the need for protein is estimated at two grams per kilogram of body weight, if this amount is provided by breast-feeding or by cow's milk in an easily digestible form. After six months, the need is somewhat less. For nursing mothers, a daily supplement of twenty to thirty grams of good quality protein is thought necessary.

When one realizes that in Europe the daily protein intake rarely goes above an average of fifty grams and that only 300,000,000 people in the world have a higher intake than this—in the Scandinavian countries, U.S.A., Canada, Australia, New Zealand and Uruguay—one becomes conscious of how much there still remains to do in this field. In South-east Asia there are 1,000,000,000 people who have less than ten grams of protein a day; while in Central Europe and in South America (Argentina and Uruguay excepted) the average varies between twenty and thirty grams.

There are other elements which affect the balance of health. These are the vitamins and certain mineral salts, calcium, sodium, iron, iodine and phosphorus being the most important. Lack of any of these can have serious consequences. Some of these are active in such small amounts that they have been called trace elements.

Our knowledge of vitamins is quite recent and continues to grow. Today we can count a score of vitamins which have been chemically analysed, the best known and the most important being: vitamin A, found in oils and animal fats and essential for vision; B[1], found in the wheat germ, the outer skin of rice and yeast, deficiency of which causes beriberi; PP, which prevents pellagra; C (ascorbic acid), which prevents scurvy; and D, which has the task of fixing calcium and making bone formation possible.

The vitamins and assimilable mineral salts are found only in certain high quality foods, such as meat, milk, cheese, which are scarce in some continents. Millions of Asiatic peoples can be said hardly to know what meat is and the average annual consumption of meat per person in Japan in 1950 was two and a quarter pounds. For more than 75 per cent of the world's population, even today, milk is a luxury.

In Basutoland, 41 per cent of people examined were found to have endemic goitre and an attempt has been made to introduce iodized salt as a preventive measure. Of recent years there has been a renewal of beriberi due to the growing habit of eating polished rice, since it is in the rough exterior of the rice grain that vitamin B[1] is contained.

It is the opinion of many doctors that a lack of mineral salts favours the development of numerous intestinal parasites. Gerard Witfield, for example, has calculated that at a time when the population of China was only 450,000,000 people, they fed some 130,000 tons of intestinal worms.[2]

One of the surest and most general symptoms of deficiency diseases in under-developed countries is a high infantile mortality rate, due very often to bad feeding of suckling infants. For a great number of these countries we possess only fragmentary statistics. Some interesting results have been obtained in Africa from enquiries set on foot by O.R.A.N.A.[3] Death-rates vary between 102 and 340 per thousand in children under one year: 63 to 130 per thousand in children between one year and two: from 298 to 419 per thousand in all children under the age of fourteen years. It is also pointed out by Dr. Tremolières that in the greater part of the population in the under-developed zones of Upper Volta, enquiries show a sudden check to growth in weight and height appearing at around six months,

[2] Quoted by Dr P. Theil, *Pour que les hommes vivent mieux*, p. 48.

[3] Organisme de Recherches sur l'Alimentation et la Nutrition en Afrique. The headquarters is in Dakar.

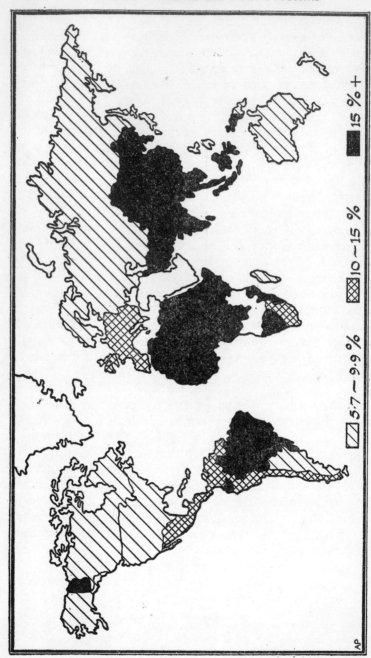

WORLD MORTALITY RATES

5·7 ~ 9.9 %   10 ~ 15 %   15 % +

becoming accentuated between ten and fifteen years of age, and then diminishing and disappearing in adolescence.

In Latin America infantile mortality rates are high, but we do not have figures such as those collected in certain parts of Africa and Asia. In those parts, almost half the children die before they reach the age of five The U.N.'s demographic service has made some estimates of infantile mortality for the period 1950–55.[4]

Annual infantile mortality rate per thousand live births
(approximate)

AMERICA
Cuba, Mexico, Paraguay 125
Bolivia, Brazil, Colombia, Ecuador, Honduras, Nicaragua, Panama, Peru, Dominican Republic, Venezuela 150
Guatemala, Salvador 175

ASIA
China (Taiwan) 100
Thailand 175
India, Pakistan, Philippines 200
Burma 225

The rates of infantile mortality shown by these figures can be more than four times those of western countries. In the countries of Western Europe, Australia and North America the figure is less than 50 per thousand, while it is usually higher than 150 per thousand for the greater part of Asia or even of Latin America. An infant in New Zealand, able to have a diet which is particularly rich in protein, has five times as much chance of surviving his first year as has an Indian or African child.

The high infantile mortality rate of the under-developed countries is also in large part the cause of the low expectation of life in those countries. M. Cépède has drawn up a table showing the expectation of life at various ages in Egypt and in France, which allows us to see how differences between the two are progressively reduced with age.[5]

[4] U.N. *Report on the state of social affairs in the world*, p. 21 (1957).
[5] M. Cépède, in *Économie Rurale*, July-Sept. 1959.

	Age					
	0	5	20	40	50	60
Egypt	35·65	54·7	59·8	66·12	69·4	73·3
France	63·6	67·7	68·4	70·4	72·2	75·1

One consequence of this difference is that the age structure of the population is quite different in developed and in under-developed countries. In the latter, the proportion of people in the income earning age groups (15 to 60) is ordinarily lower than in the former.

There is also a connection between nutrition and aptitude for work. A bad diet is at once translated into low labour productivity. In many cases, it is only necessary to improve the diet to bring about an increase in productivity.

In the under-developed countries, where the people are usually badly fed, it is difficult to make native workers as productive as Europeans are. This is more a matter of dietary deficiencies than, as was at one time thought, of race. Numerous examples have shown that when the diet of workpeople is improved and they are assured of substantial nourishment, they become capable of a work output which is the equal, in duration and intensity of effort, of that of other workers. It is for this reason that many undertakings in Africa, for example, habitually provide works canteens where their employees can find better meals than they could in their homes or anywhere else. Not only is output raised, but also there is less absenteeism and fewer accidents.

In Ruanda-Urundi, employers are unanimous in recognizing the great benefit of a well cooked and balanced meal provided by the undertaking. Indeed, some of them estimate that productivity rises by some 30 per cent because of it. This opinion is also expressed in the Federation of Rhodesia and Nyasaland. There is also the example of an undertaking in Gaboon which employs workpeople from the Lake Chad region. This business distributes a ration of millet and fresh fish, not only to its employees, but also to their families. The state of health of these workers is excellent: so much so that, while the absenteeism of the Gaboon workers is 0·99 per cent, that of the men from Lake Chad is only 0·46 per cent. A sugar refinery in Madagascar reports the same experience: there labour turnover has been reduced from 60 per cent to 6 per cent, partly by better feeding, and productivity has in consequence risen considerably.[6]

It is, of course, possible, and one sees it in eastern countries, for a man to adapt himself to a reduced food supply, even to a semi-famine diet, without endangering his life; but repercussions in other directions are formidable. As an F.A.O. report observes:

> The entire mode of life is organized around the fact of an insufficiency of calories in the diet and the results of this are socially deplorable. There is a lack of energy and initiative; a refusal to face physical or intellectual effort; a tendency to sleep too much. There is, in addition, diminished resistance to certain types of sickness and a lowered ability to recuperate after a sickness.[7]

It is well known that with children, under-feeding causes irregular attendance at school and poor attention in class. Enquiries into this aspect which have been made in Haiti have produced significant results.

> Most of the pupils arrive at school after a breakfast consisting only of some fruit. Almost all of them must wait until evening for the main meal of the day. Some parents do not send their children to school because they cannot often give them a meal before evening. The children are well accustomed to such a meagre existence, but the effects of their bad feeding are visible all the same. They cannot pay attention for long and are very soon inclined to fall asleep. After a few hours, it becomes very difficult to get them to make the slightest intellectual effort.[8]

In Upper Volta and in other places, many children living in the bush have to walk four or five miles to school with only a handful of millet in their stomachs and wait until evening before they can eat again, unless the mission school is able to give them a ration of milk or some vitaminized biscuits.

[6] C.C.T.A. enquiry into *Les Facteurs humains de la productivité en Afrique*, pp. 18 and 31.

[7] F.A.O. *Calory Needs*, p. 12.

[8] U.N.E.S.C.O., *Experiment in Haiti*, p. 34.

A missionary in Duala, in the Cameroons, has estimated recently that 90 per cent of native children in the town are ill-fed and hungry.

Illnesses arising from defective feeding—famine excepted—cover quite a range and have lesser or greater effects on the human organism. They are classified according to the clinical symptoms: beriberi, pellagra, scurvy, nutritional anaemia and kwashiorkor (malignant malnutrition), this last being a formidable type of protein deficiency in children.

In the under-developed countries, many more people suffer from these maladies, and are thereby condemned to lead a sickly existence subject to all sorts of ills, than are stricken with other types of disease. But the period when the diet is most important is unquestionably between weaning and adolescence. In the poor lands, the child is at this stage of its life abandoned to its own devices. It has to live as best it can, with little help from its parents, who are themselves generally under-nourished.

It is usually after weaning that the dramatic symptoms appear of the deficiency of proteins (often associated with that of certain vitamins) which has been given the African name of kwashiorkor, meaning in the Bantu dialect, red child. The infant swells up with oedema and its hair becomes dry and

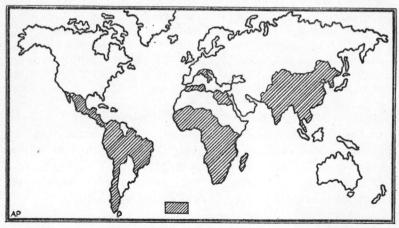

THE GEOGRAPHICAL DISTRIBUTION OF KWASHIORKOR

reddened. It loses weight and ceases to grow, while its skin becomes distorted and changes colour. It becomes pot-bellied. The child grows apathetic and dejected, weakens and dies.

This disease, from which children do not suffer so long as they are being fed at the breast, is very common in tropical countries, especially in Africa and in certain parts of South and Central America, and is also met with in Asia. It often takes milder forms which are more difficult to diagnose, but these also are very harmful for the child's development. The cause of it is now well known: it arises out of an insufficiency of protein in the child's diet.

Widespread scientific investigations into the disease during the past ten years have thrown a great deal of light on the matter. A mission from F.A.O. and W.H.O. visited Central and Tropical Africa in 1950 to discover the incidence of the disease. Investigations were carried out in Kenya, Uganda, Ruanda-Urundi, the former Belgian Congo, French Equatorial Africa, Nigeria, Ghana, Liberia, Gambia and Senegal.

In those areas where the disease is widespread it was found that meat eating people, such as the Masai of Kenya, and those who consumed large quantities of milk did not get kwashiorkor. On the other hand, those tribes which had a diet deficient in proteins, both as regards quality and quantity—the main ingredients being cassava, plantains, yams and maize—always had a high incidence of the disease.

> There is no kwashiorkor among the Basuti, a pastoral people of Ruanda and Urundi, who drink a lot of curdled milk. There is among the Bahutu, who live in the same parts as the Basuti, but are farmers who feed their children mainly on plantains, cassava, maize and sweet potatoes. [9]

Similarly, the disease is rare among peoples who dwell beside rivers or lakes and can easily obtain supplies of fish. Vincent gives the result of his investigation:

> You would not find the disease on the shores of Lake Tanganyika, where fresh and dried fish are abundant in the markets. But you would find it within six miles of the lake, where fish is already more scarce.

[9] J. F. Brook and M. Autret, *Kwashiorkor in Africa*, p. 46. (F.A.O., 1952.)

The bad feeding of children is to be explained in terms of the African family custom of eating out of a common dish. Weaning does not usually take place earlier than sixteen or eighteen months of age, but the infant is then submitted brusquely to the family diet and takes the consequences.

From the moment that the child has to take his place around the common dish, he cannot hope to have any of the tit-bits. It is the men's privilege to serve themselves first and to take such pieces of meat or fish as there are. It is not a question of child neglect, for the African negro is very fond of his children. But it is always the custom among the poor —and not only in Africa—for the breadwinner to be best fed. As long as the family has not enough food to satisfy the needs of all, the young child will have long periods during which he will have to make do with the starchy foods, and he will waste much of that. The growth curve of children up to the age of seven or eight years shows this quantitative and qualitative deficiency in the diet; but this is more striking among boys, for the girls cluster more about the mother and get some pieces while the meals are being prepared. Later the children look after themselves better, as much about the family dish as outside the cabin, in the fields and forest.[10]

Dr Leon Pales, one of the founders of O.R.A.N.A. at Dakar, writes:

Between the time when a child leaves its mother's breast and enters upon adolescence there is no transitional stage in its diet, but only a ditch which not all pass over.

To all of this we have to add the fact that the African child already carries within itself the effects of its mother's dietary deficiencies. It weighs less than does a white child. Investigators note that

in most parts of Africa, the expectant mother receives no special nutritional aid. Right up to her confinement she carries on with her work in the house and in the fields. Afterwards, she takes them up again too soon, if indeed she has interrupted them for a day or so. Her diet will remain the same as it has always been.[11]

[10] J. F. Brook and M. Autret, *Kwashiorkor in Africa*, p. 44. (F.A.O., 1952.)
[11] Ibid.

What remedy can be found for this state of affairs? The problem is first of all to find a good substitute for cow's milk to feed the child properly after it has been weaned, for milk cannot be produced in sufficient quantities in Africa. As for condensed or powdered milk, for a long time to come they will be beyond the purchasing power of the mass of the people.

Use of vegetable oils derived from peanuts or soya-beans, which Africans can prepare themselves, can give good results. Peanut oil is prepared in the native pestle, the concentration being one-third of a pound of peanuts, lightly roasted, to one and three-quarter pints of water. The mixture is filtered through a cloth and then boiled for ten minutes. It can be used for infants from the age of four or five months. Although it is certainly not the ideal food for a child, it is of a much higher nutritional value in proteins than any preparation made by boiling starchy foods such as cassava, plantains or maize.

Systematic trials have been made by O.R.A.N.A., with the collaboration of the Children's Fund, in areas where a protein deficiency has been established. The main experiment was made in a district of Senegal, where a distribution of powdered milk was made to pregnant and nursing women and to children under the age of five, and on a selective basis to children between five and ten. A similar method was applied in Upper Volta and the Ivory Coast, where a medical check was kept on 3,800 children during a lengthy period. The results show a high percentage of cures where nutritional troubles already existed and an absence of new cases among those who had been protected, even though the previous rate of infection reached 40 per cent of children weaned, and an important fall in the rate of infantile mortality

Experiments have also been made with fish, powdered or in the form of a paste, a food which is rich in assimilable nitrogen and also in vitamins and other oligo-elements. It is a most valuable product, the use of which is, however, most unhappily limited—like powdered milk—because of its cost.[12]

Finally, it is very important that action be taken, at the same time, to educate African women and convince them of the

[12] Report of Drs Senegal and Raoult to Journées Medicales d'Outre-Mer, Strasbourg, 1955.

need to improve their children's diet, for, in the last resort, it is on them that improvement of the situation depends.

In 1953, F.A.O. and W.H.O. conducted another enquiry into protein deficiencies in five states of Brazil, Belem, Recife, Rio de Janeiro, Belo Horizonte and Porto Alegre.

The Brazilian infant is weaned much earlier than the African, often between five and nine months and sometimes as early as three months. As in Africa, the infant remains healthy for as long as it is breast-fed, and so the work began by giving complements to the diet, varying with the locality. Usually, children are fed on a gruel made of starchy foods, to which is added a small amount of sugar and sometimes a little milk, but milk is scarce and expensive in the districts visited by the investigators. In some districts, children are also given haricot soup. But this diet, while it is rich in starch, is deficient in proteins and other nutritional elements and this causes a high rate of *distrofia pluricarencial*, the name given locally to kwashiorkor.

Figures supplied by hospitals in Rio and in Belo Horizonte show that, in these cities, kwashiorkor is the cause of one-fourth of all admissions. At least another quarter is of ill-nourished people, even when the principal cause of admission to hospital is different. Numerous cases are reported from the district of Porto Alegre of malnutrition among infants under one year of age. Prof. Moreira estimates that 70 per cent of the children admitted to hospital are badly fed.

Many children at and below school age are in a condition bordering on chronic malnutrition.

> We have taken advantage of every opportunity which has been offered to us to examine, at random, children living in the poor urban districts. They were weighed on portable scales and the figures obtained, while they lack precision, are enough to give a general idea of the situation. Of the 200 children examined, of ages ranging from two to eight years, one-third weighed at least 20 per cent less than normal.[13]

In the countries visited in Central America, the situation was a little better. Guatemala, Honduras, Nicaragua, Costa Rica

[13] J. Waterlow and A. Vergara, *Protein deficiency in Brazil.* (F.A.O. 1957.)

and Panama are countries in the tropical zone, the poor population being for the most part engaged in agriculture. The enquiry concludes:

> The many and often serious cases seen at the consulting rooms and even in the villages themselves leave no room for doubt. Protein deficiency is much more widespread than the medical statistics show. Dietary deficiency is clear, beginning at the moment the child moves to a mixed diet, and is often critical at the time of weaning and the period immediately afterwards. The effect on the nutritional condition of the infant is immediate.[14]

In Brazil and in Central America the struggle against protein deficiency in children is going on. There is a development of centres for mother and child care. Children of school age are given an addition to the diet, in the form of powdered skimmed milk, in a growing number of schools, particularly in towns. It is more difficult to deal with the situation in the rural areas, partly because of a lack of qualified personnel and also because most of the children in the backward areas do not go to school. The enquiries emphasize the necessity of extending distributions from the urban centres into other parts of the country.

Absence of some vitamins, and vitamin B in particular, can cause serious types of nutritional disease which can be killing, as with acute cases of beriberi.

Rice eaters in several countries in South and East Asia, notably Burma, Thailand and Viet-Nam, to this day offer a serious problem of beriberi to the public health authorities. Investigations made on behalf of W.H.O. in these countries reveal a high death rate among breast-fed infants under the age of six months. Outbreaks of the disease have been reported from some rice areas in the countryside in Eastern Asia. Up to the last war, in those parts, the people had preserved the practice of grinding their own rice in the old-fashioned pestle, a process which lost little of the husk. But for some years now they have been using small mechanical huskers to give a whiter rice, poor in thiamine, which upsets the balance of the people's diet. This repeats what had already happened in the towns with

[14] M. Autret and M. Behar, *Le Syndrome de polycarence de l'enfance en Amérique centrale* (1955).

the use of milled rice from which the husk which contains the vitamin B has been removed.

Beriberi levies a high price also in India and Ceylon, both rice eating countries. One of its most tragic forms is acute beriberi, which attacks individuals most harshly and causes a particularly high infant mortality among children of from two to four months. According to Dr Jelliffe, this disease is so common in Viet-Nam as to merit its title of a scourge of society. This author estimates that in the town of Bien-Hoa, one-quarter of the deaths of children below the age of one are caused by it. The peasants think of it as a "ghost disease", one that is spread by an evil spirit who eats up the souls of children, and this superstition stands in the way of medical treatment, since it is to the village sorcerer that people go in the first instance.

The cause of the disease is perfectly well known now and we possess the means for its prevention and treatment. For proof of this there is the example of Japan, in which beriberi was widespread during the first quarter of the twentieth century. The Japanese have perfected a method of enriching rice with several derivatives or compounds of thiamine to make what is called *polyrice*. The Japanese housewives know how to make good use of it and, as a result, beriberi has almost completely disappeared from the country.[15] The same thing has been observed in the Philippines, where the consumption of enriched rice was followed by a considerable fall in the number of deaths from this disease.

There is another form of vitamin deficiency which is met with in areas where the diet is but little varied and is based on maize. This is pellagra, with its eruptions of erythema, accompanied often by inflammation of the tongue and gastro-intestinal trouble, provoking a state of cachexy which can end in death.

Recent research has shown that pellagra is connected with a diet usually based on maize and deficient in vitamin PP (niacine) and in proteins of good quality. In Basutoland it is known as *lefu la pone*, that is to say, the maize sickness. It was common at one time in the southern states of U.S.A. and in Italy; and

[15] In 1955 the production of thiamine in Japan totalled nearly 100,000 lb., of which over 65,000 lb. was exported. The price was £3 a lb.: or 4 cents, U.S. per milligramme. After allowing for exports, there remained enough to give the whole population a daily dose of 0·48 milligrammes each. (*Report of the Committee for Nutrition in South and East Asia*, 4th session, 1956.)

it is still met with in the countries of Latin America, Puerto Rico, Portugal, India and Southern Rhodesia.

The sickness can be treated with nicotinic acid. A demonstration programme set on foot in Yugoslavia has proved that the addition of niacine to the maize in the small handmills is an efficacious remedy against pellagra. In countries where the disease is associated with a high consumption of maize (often 60 per cent), it is recommended that agricultural and educational programmes should insist on the necessity of increasing the consumption of cereals other than maize, or of vegetables and other foodstuffs which can assure a better balance in the diet.

It is recognized today that many eye troubles, some of which can cause permanent blindness, are allied with nutritional deficiencies, particularly with a lack of vitamin A.

This type of vitamin deficiency is very common in certain tropical areas, and particularly in the south-east of Asia. It is also found in the eastern Mediterranean region, along the coasts of North Africa and in parts of South America. But it is in the Indies and Indonesia that it is particularly prevalent.

It is the young children who are most often attacked. In a study of 9,000 cases undertaken by ophthalmologists in Indonesia, it was found that 4 per cent were of children under one, 83 per cent of children between one and six, 6 per cent between seven and fifteen, and 7 per cent sixteen and over. Dr Jelliffe has observed cases of vitamin A deficiency in the hospitals of all the Indian towns he has visited, as well as in the village of Najagarth, near New Delhi. "In one household of the village, visited quite unexpectedly, three children out of six were affected. In Ceylon, it has been known for some years that infants and children often show vitamin deficiency. In the opinion of A. Nicholls, 60 per cent of the cases of blindness observed in Ceylon and in Southern India are the result of an earlier keratomalacia."[16]

Experiments on animals have shown that a large number of pathological eye conditions can be brought about by a defective diet. Vitamin A deficiency, a cause of a high death rate among infants, can also cause serious ophthalmic troubles in later years. The eye can continue to look quite normal in the early

[16] Dr Jelliffe, *L'Alimentation des Nourrissons dans les régions tropicales et subtropicales*, p. 88.

stages of a vitamin A deficiency, even if the patient already suffers from hemeralophy and reveals a considerable loss of vision as soon as the light is reduced or lowered. Later, when the clinical symptoms on the cornea are apparent, deterioration becomes rapid and only immediate treatment can then prevent an incurable lesion on the cornea.

Clinical studies in many countries which are particularly threatened have shown that concentrates of carotene, taken orally, give good results in the treatment of xerophthalmia. These successes indicate that a substantial addition of carotene to diets which are deficient in vitamin A and in proteins can prevent the appearance of the disease.

Where the diet does not bring about a manifestation of serious nutritional defects, the pathological effects of malnutrition can sometimes take curious combined and attenuated forms. Thus, in one district of Mauritania where the diet is frugal but where the people use goat milk, investigation by probing carried out by Dr Mazer brought to light only minor forms of malnutrition, serious enough however to show the need for an improvement in the diet. Out of 583 children examined, he found pathological violaceous or oedematous gums, with or without a loosening of the teeth, in 64 children between one and fourteen years of age; swollen stomachs or umbilical hernias in 19 of the same age group; and also 23 cases of pigmented tongue and 18 of dry skin and hyperkeratosity. He found also 23 cases of abnormal pigmentation (traces of blue) in the conjunctiva of the eye, attributed to vitamin A deficiency.[17]

The inhabitants of Mauritius show another form of dietary deficiency, ferric anaemia due to the absence of certain mineral salts. Cases are so numerous as to constitute a problem of public health. In 1955, there were 43,277 cases of anaemia notified in a population of 500,000, and there are indications that the real total of cases is even higher. Enquiries have shown that the anaemia is relatively rare in the wealthier parts of the island but common in the poorer parts, where it could attack up to 30 per cent of the juveniles.

In most cases, the anaemia can be easily dealt with by the administration of iron in small doses. The cost of the tablets

[17] "Enquête-sondage alimentation-nutrition faite dans le Hodh", *Bulletin de l'Institut National d'Hygiène*, Sept.–Oct. 1959.

of sulphate of iron that were distributed to children in the schools in the course of the investigation is less than that of the cocoa that is added to their milk. In the treatment of most of the cases of anaemia in Mauritius it has been recognized that injections of vitamins and of liver extract are largely useless and superfluous, besides being much more burdensome.

Many specialists think that the bad sanitary conditions found in under-developed countries are not unconnected with protein deficiencies, because of the intestinal infections to which they give rise. Bacterial infections are very frequent in the unhealthy milieu in which most of the children in tropical countries are reared. The mixed committee of experts from W.H.O. and the Children's Fund came to the following conclusions: "Probably three-quarters of the world's population drink impure water, evacuate their excreta without taking any precaution, prepare milk and other foodstuffs in dangerous conditions, are constantly exposed to contact with insects and rats, and live in unhealthy dwellings."[18]

In these conditions there is a complete failure of sanitation and it is no cause for wonder that ill-nourished and susceptible children pay a heavy price by way of all sorts of infections: of the throat and lungs in overcrowded dwellings, draughty and damp; of the skin, by scabies, from insect bites and dirt; and, above all, intestinal, the result of using dirty kitchen utensils, dirty hands and unboiled, contaminated water.[19]

Nobody is now ignorant of the fact that a diet can be too rich in certain substances (fat, in particular) and that this creates a danger to public health in countries enjoying a high standard of living.

In these countries, the classic nutritional deficiencies are of relatively minor importance, compared with the metabolic troubles of adults, vascular and arthritic conditions in particular.

There is now an abundance of proof that diet plays an important part in the development of degenerative cardiac conditions, among them coronary troubles, angina pectoris

[18] Quoted in the Fifth Report of the Joint Committee of F.A.O. and W.H.O.
[19] Dr Jelliffe, loc. cit., p. 127.

and myocardiac degeneration. These cardiopathic conditions have become the most frequent cause of death in North America and in a large part of Europe, particularly among the wealthier elements in the population.[20]

For some years now, doctors have been agreed that the countries where the diet is particularly rich in fat are also those in which heart attacks are most frequent. A high level of cholesterol in the blood appears to have some connection with the number of serious attacks, such as angina pectoris and infarct of the myocardium. It is known that the deposits of cholesterol in the arteries reduce their diameter, and that this brings many, often serious, disorders in its train.

A gathering of international specialists in Paris in 1960 to discuss these matters showed that there is still much that is obscure. Nevertheless, it seems to be established beyond doubt that there is a connection between nutrition and cardio-vascular diseases. As early as 1955, the joint committee of F.A.O. and W.H.O. advocated "the educative and other measures which would be necessary to give this view practical expression in the field of preventive medicine and public health".

There are already remedies to hand to lower the level of cholesterol in the blood, but their use is a delicate matter. It seems that at present the most efficacious line of approach is by way of the diet. A reduction in the quantity of animal fat in the diet, particularly with people who are not physically very active, offers a by no means negligible measure of protection against serious cardio-vascular disorders.

[20] F.A.O.–W.H.O. Joint Committee, 1955, p. 47.

V

SEEKING OUT THE BADLY FED

THANKS to a great deal of research, by way of experiments, observations and meticulous laboratory analyses, we have today at our disposal the principles of a science of nutrition, telling us the nutritive value of every type of food. Thus we know better than we did before what are the needs of the human organism and how they may be satisfied. The work of Mme Randoin, in France, has put the question of what constitutes a balanced diet upon a scientific basis.[1]

It would be going too far to say that a science which is as yet only in its infancy has already thrown light upon every question. There are still areas of darkness which invite further investigation. The structure of a living being is very complex and the interactions of its various elements hard to unravel.

In what follows we shall first refer to certain fundamental points and then try to present in brief outline a statement of the enquiries into questions of nutrition which have been made of recent years in several of the under-developed countries.

Theoretical standards of calory needs have been set up by a committee of F.A.O. These standards are generally accepted and most nutritionists today use them for a point of reference. The method consists in establishing the energy requirements of a standard person and then correcting for variations of age, body weight, surrounding temperature and activity.

The standard man and woman are 25 years of age, live in the temperate zone where the temperature is around 10 degrees centigrade (50 degrees fahrenheit), enjoy a well-balanced diet and are in perfect health. The man's degree of activity is taken to be that required of a skilled artisan and the woman's is that of a housewife or an employee in a small-scale business. The expenditure of energy, calculated on an annual basis, is esti-

---

[1] Mme Lucie Randoin, *Les Rations alimentaires équilibrées* (5th edit.).

mated to require a daily calory intake of 3,200 and 2,300 calories respectively.

These are average figures and must be modified according to the circumstances. Thus, a nursing mother needs 1,000 more calories a day and an eighteen year old boy needs a daily intake of 3,800 calories. The F.A.O. committee recommended that 160 and 115 calories should be added to or subtracted from the basic daily rations for men and women for every fall or rise of 10 degrees centigrade in the outside temperature.

Using this basis to estimate the needs of a whole population, Dr Theil concludes that

> the food situation is satisfactory if, on average, individuals have at their disposal 3,000 calories a day. If there are only 2,300 to 2,500 available, there is under-nourishment. Below 2,000 is a state of acute shortage. Around 1,500 we can speak of a famine, while below 1,000—and this was the situation in the Nazi concentration camps—death must ensue if the shortage is prolonged.[2]

It is clear, however, that in such a "human" matter scientific methods appear inadequate. Neither the idea of under-nourishment nor that of the standard prototype adopted by nutritionists can enable us to deal fully with a phenomenon some details of which must escape scientific observation. These conclusions must, therefore, be treated as no more than provisional hypotheses, as the report of the committee of experts points out.

> They will have to be modified as new research into the theoretical and practical problems of nutrition and improvement in the techniques of field study give us a clearer view of the ways in which health is connected with feeding.[3]

Several studies have already been undertaken to assess the value and the deficiencies of the standard table of nutritional requirements, as also of the way in which these have been used. It is clear that we cannot pretend to more than approximations in this field and that nutritional standards call for judicious inter-

[2] Pierre Theil, op. cit., p. 30.
[3] *Report of Second Committee on Calory Needs*, p. 5 (F.A.O., 1957).

pretation. We shall see in what follows how delicate the task of the investigator is.

Despite the difficulties in the way, it is still most urgently necessary to proceed with nutritional enquiries in the under-developed countries, rather than in areas which have a higher standard of living, given that one of the purposes of these enquiries is to determine the relationship between diets and the deficiency diseases which are so common in those countries.

It is for this reason that investigation has been proceeding in several provinces of India, particularly in those parts where beriberi is prevalent. Other enquiries have been made in parts of Africa, special attention being paid to West Africa—Ivory Coast, Upper Volta, Senegal and Gambia—in efforts to discover the causes of the multiform nutritional deficiency which gives rise to kwashiorkor. In Java attention has been directed to those regions where there is a deficiency of vitamin A. In Puerto Rico the purpose has been to establish a basis for a programme of education.

Experience has amply shown the need for caution in this field and how necessary it is to avoid hasty and insufficiently grounded generalizations which, to a greater or lesser extent, give a deformed picture of reality. Only truly rigorous research will furnish useful information on the exact qualitative and quantitative value of the habitual diets in different countries and in different parts of the same country.

There is often a great variation in habitual diets in one and the same country, the food of pastoral tribes, for example, being quite different from that of settled agricultural tribes. Furthermore, there is no standardization in methods of preparing food and the value of different foodstuffs can vary considerably according to the method of preparation.

Laboratory analysis of a certain number of elements will sometimes form a preliminary stage of an investigation. Thus, in West Africa care was taken to collect, classify and analyse a large number of foodstuffs used by families or on sale in the markets, some of the analyses being done in Dakar and others in Paris. In Brazil, Professor Josué de Castro found that the most serious obstacle met with in the course of his enquiries was the lack of information on the composition of the foodstuffs consumed in each locality.

Some foods are more completely digested than others. Thus, for example, milled rice is better assimilated than are some varieties of millet, of which the cellulose content is relatively high. It can be very useful, therefore, to use a coefficient of digestibility when making an investigation, and this will necessitate the working out of different tables. It is also of importance to bear in mind that fruits and drinks do not appear in the diets that are studied, because more often than not, in Africa, fruit is picked and eaten outside the house, between meals. In the period before the gathering of the new crop these fruits can do much to supplement the insufficiency of the family's meals. Drinks such as millet beer or palm wine are not taken every day but only on certain occasions.[4]

It is important to bear in mind, therefore, that quite a wide gap may exist between the official estimates supplied by the administrative services and the actual situation. In his study on the food problem in South America, Josué de Castro tells us the food supply in Bolivia, Chile, Peru and Ecuador does not reach 2,000 calories a day. But he adds this:

> Happily, the true situation is not so bad. . . . These people generally have a greater supply of calories than the figures given above would indicate. It is usual in the primitive parts for these peoples to have at their disposal several foodstuffs the nature of which is almost always unknown to and which, therefore, are not taken into account by the specialists when they are calculating the calory content of the diet. Finally, statistics do not account for all the foodstuffs that are consumed, because isolated groups with an almost feudal economy consume part of what they produce.

Quite apart from these possibilities of error, we have also to bear in mind that average figures worked out on a national basis conceal large differences between levels of nutrition in different parts of the population, by reason of geographical variations and differences in economic and professional status and in age. Since what is important is the connection between diet and health, the only way in which we can obtain the indispensable details is to make enquiries into the circumstances of representative samples of the population in question.

[4] Léon Pales, *L'Alimentation en A.O.F.*, p. 209.

The organization of any enquiry of some importance raises numerous problems of the choice and size of samples, length of the enquiry, recruitment of investigators and their training for the task in hand, and finally the often delicate task of interpreting the results.

Ordinarily, it does not appear to be useful to visit a large number of families: the quality of the information gathered is more important than a multiplication of facts which lack precision. In the villages of Africa it is often enough to study 10 or 15 households, provided that one is not at the same time enquiring into household budgets. That calls for a study of a greater number of families, the more so if incomes are very unequal, as they are in the cocoa and coffee growing areas.

The method of enquiry should take into account the pattern of farm work, as also of festival and market days, which sometimes sensibly modify the general run of household menus. For this reason, too, households ought to be visited every day for a number of days at different times. Much importance must usually be attached to seasonal variations in under-developed countries because of the close connection which there is between production and consumption of home-produced foodstuffs. We cannot expect to have a reliable knowledge of diets unless our enquiries are pursued at different times of the year.

The selection of investigators is not always easy. Preferably, they should be selected locally wherever there are to be found people who are able to do the work and can be spared to do it. Such people must be able, after a brief training, to make a careful record of the number of people being fed and work out a table of weights of each element entering into the diet. Investigators must, of course, be provided with portable scales, as also with forms setting out the headings under which they must set down, each day, the information collected about each family. At every meal they should note the number of people eating, with particulars of age and sex, and the presence of any pregnant or nursing women. It is difficult for one investigator to enquire into the diets of more than one family at a time. In exceptional circumstances, he might do two or three. The advantage of recruiting local people, and particularly local women, is that they know the eating habits of the people and understand the local dialect and so can more easily obtain the confidence of the families into whose habits they are enquiring.

Even so, no matter how skilled the investigators may be, those who are responsible for the conduct of the enquiry must be careful always to keep a careful check on the accuracy of the returns. "Nobody who has once applied such a check can doubt the utility of making it. In the same way, it is absolutely necessary for those who are responsible for the investigation to make regular visits to the village to watch their investigators at work. Not only is this the only way in which they can guard against idleness on the part of the investigators, it is also the only way in which they can discover for themselves the difficulties in the way of carrying out their own instructions."[5]

Depending upon the care with which an enquiry is carried out, F.A.O. experts estimate that errors of fact can be as great as 10, 20, or even 50 per cent. Examples of such enquiries are not hard to find. There was one on the pattern of day to day family spending which was based on information collected in the course of a single interview; another on nutrition which neglected food that workers found in the fields; and another in which the numbers of people being fed were not checked accurately enough.

An enquiry of a type carried out among the Agnis people at Bougouanou, on the Ivory Coast, shows clearly the sort of difficulties which have sometimes to be surmounted. This people has a strongly developed sense of community which shows itself, at meal times, in a general post of cooked dishes among the housewives; and, to make matters more confusing, in a custom for the men and young people almost daily to be invited or to invite themselves to eat outside their own family circle. Then there are the frequent moves around the farm camps.[6] It frequently happens that a housewife will leave her kitchen to stay with the workers on the plantation and in her absence the remainder of her family will eat with neighbours. The investigators had to keep track of all these details; evidently, not a simple task.

---

[5] Monthly bulletin of F.A.O., Jan. 1959.

[6] The coffee and cocoa plantations are usually quite a long way away from the village; and whenever the work requires it, the custom is to live on the job in simple huts erected there.

A quick check made by O.R.A.N.A. at the village of Dialakoro, some kilometres distant from Bamako, gives us a glimpse of the thin diets to which most of the families are restricted in the period before harvest, when the stocks of food are low. The total number of people in the families investigated was 759, with an average daily intake of 802 calories. Of these people, 70 per cent had less than 1,000 calories a day; 25 per cent had from 1,000 to 1,999 calories; only 5 per cent had more than 2,000 calories. The food of four of the families investigated consisted of no more than millet bran cooked with a few leaves from the gourd. It is obvious that such a diet is representative of only one short period of the year; but the example shows how necessary it is to conduct enquiries over a sufficiently lengthy period if we want to have a true picture of a people's diet.

In the same way, it is often necessary to make allowance for festival days when reckoning what the diet is. For example, among the Senoufo the ordinary menu is based on millet accompanied with a fish sauce or groundnuts and has an estimated daily value of 2,586 calories a head. However, when account is taken of the quite frequent festival days the average daily ration rises to about 2,750 calories. Some things like rice and meat are kept for festival days only and not infrequently on such days the people eat enormous meals, worth as much as 4,657 calories a head.[7]

It is evident that it is a difficult enough matter to carry out an enquiry into nutrition in conditions such as these, but the interpretation of results creates even more difficulties. This task cannot be given to any save experienced authorities on nutritional problems, and even so, the evaluation of results is always a long process.[8]

[7] D. Malgras, *La condition sociale du paysan minyanka dans le Cercle de San.*

[8] The notion of the African family as a food consuming unit is difficult to grasp. Dr Tremolières notes that in consequence of this some aspects of nutrition which are closely bound up with the household economy escape us. One of these is the problem of the influence which family size exerts on food consumption. "Enquiries in Upper Volta, where this matter has been investigated, indicate that in Africa, as elsewhere, the level of feeding drops considerably as the numbers of children rise. Among the groups investigated, the calorific value of the diets of large families (reckoned by the intake per head) is considerably lower than that of the diets of small families of one or two children. There is a reduction of 20 to 30 per cent for the family with six or seven children, and of 40 to 50 per cent for the family with more than ten children." (Dr Tremolières, writing in the *Bulletin de l'Institut National d'Hygiène*, Oct.–Dec., 1957, p. 746.)

We can list here the essentials discovered by a number of investigations in various parts of the world, the results produced having similar characteristics, despite differences in techniques employed.[9]

An investigation was undertaken by O.R.A.N.A., in 1957, in a district on the lower Senegal River between Dagana and Bakel. This district is 12½ miles wide by 230 miles long, quite fertile, at the junction of a cereal growing and a cattle rearing zone and lying along a river rich in fish.

The investigation, which lasted for a year, showed an average daily intake per person of 2,175 calories, well balanced in quality except for vitamins A and C. A deficiency of vitamin A was quite common, showing itself in a reduction of vision at dusk. The supply of vitamin C, while being also insufficient, did not fall below the minimum level.

In its conclusions, the enquiry pointed to the necessity of making the largest practicable increase in the domestic output of foodstuffs with a higher vitamin content. It suggested a greater consumption of fish, rich in vitamin A; and the development of fruit growing, very neglected in the valley, to supply vitamin C, the value of which in building up resistance against infectious diseases is emphasized.

An enquiry among the Ouatchi people of South Togoland, in the important village of Attitogon, situated about 40 miles to the north-east of Lome and about 20 miles from the sea, covered 799 persons in 148 households. It was made over three separate periods of a year, in May, September and January, so as to cover variations in diet over the seasons.

The calorific value of the diet was satisfactory on the whole, when compared with theoretical needs, there being a small deficit in the pre-harvest period when maize supplies are running out. Because the diet consisted as to 80 per cent of maize and cassava, there was a deficiency of fats and proteins. Moreover, the diet was badly balanced in that there was only a small availability of protective foods, such as meat, fish and vegetables.

[9] In its summary of nutritional enquiries, published in 1958, the F.A.O. listed 57 investigations carried out in 30 different countries. Of these, 26 were in Europe, 6 in North America, 7 in Central and South America, 1 in the Near East (Israel), 9 in the Far East (Ceylon, India, Japan, Philippines) and 8 in Africa (former French Equatorial Africa, Egypt, Ghana, Union of South Africa).

The investigation pointed to a need to increase the output of cereals, of which there was a bare sufficiency. This can be done by introducing higher yielding varieties of maize and by improving methods of storage. On the other hand, it also emphasized the need to remedy the deficiency of proteins in the diet. For this, the method would be an educational programme, which would lead to an improvement in the feeding of the vulnerable groups (pregnant and nursing women and infants being weaned) and action against the ritual bans and the prejudices which are still active among the tribes.

An investigation in 1955–56 among the Agni people of Bougouanou (Ivory Coast), a district in the equatorial forest, showed that the people, coffee and cocoa growers, suffered from under-nourishment to only a small degree.[10] The diet was somewhat unbalanced, however, there being an excess of starchy foods and a deficiency of fats and proteins. Starchy foodstuffs supplied 81 per cent of the diet, only 8 per cent being provided by fats and 11 per cent from proteins, of which $3\frac{1}{2}$ per cent was of animal origin. Nevertheless, the protein deficiency is not such as to cause serious physiological disorders. Among 2,819 village children examined, there were only 11 cases of protein malnutrition observed: among these being one case of pre-kwashiorkor and ten cases of the disease in its first and second stages, with no case at all in stage three.

On the whole, this is a satisfactory state of affairs. It is due to the relatively high standard of life attained by the growers of coffee and cocoa, who are able to buy foodstuffs rich in animal protein, such as meat and fish.[11]

[10] *Enquête Nutrition-Niveau de vie*, subdistrict of Bougouanou, 1955–56.

[11] The F.A.O. Bulletin, Jan. 1959, publishes some results from the various enquiries carried out in West Africa during the last few years. 1. Everywhere, 75 to 80 per cent of the calories are supplied by cereals and tubers. In the less favoured areas, calories derived from animal products do not supply more than 8 per cent of the total, while fruits and vegetables supply less than 5 per cent. This lack of balance in the diet is the cause of most of the deficiencies met with: kwashiorkor and vitamin deficiencies. 2. In general, hunger is not to be found in areas which depend mainly upon tubers, the gross calory yield per acre being high (cassava and yams yield $2\frac{1}{4}$ to $4\frac{1}{2}$ million calories to the acre). However, there is evidence enough of malnutrition among the more vulnerable sections of the population. In the areas which depend mainly on cereals, the situation is less good: the gross calory yield is lower ($\frac{1}{2}$ to $1\frac{1}{2}$ million units to the acre) and the rainfall is usually more capricious. The pre-harvest period is often critical; and it would be advantageous, therefore, to extend enquiries over several years so as to discover how underfeeding varies from one year to another.

An enquiry into the feeding of school children in Morocco was set on foot in collaboration with the Institut National d'Hygiène de Paris in 1955, the object being to discover the extent and the nature of improvements in diets that would be desirable. The investigation was conducted in four localities: Casablanca, typical of the great modern and rapidly growing towns with an important Jewish quarter; Marakesh, representing the traditional town; Sidi Rahal, a typical lowland village, which was helped with food supplied by A.J.D.C. (a charitable organization supported by the United Jewish Appeal); and Asni, a village in the mountains.

The investigation showed that, during the week, the diets were from 20 to 30 per cent deficient in calories and proteins, with a deficiency of animal protein of 50 to 80 per cent. This deficiency of animal protein was almost the same for girls and boys between the ages of 6 and 15 years.

In the village of Asni, however, the use of buttermilk considerably reduced the deficiency in animal protein. While in both the villages calory deficiency was very small, in the towns it was well in excess of 20 per cent. This calory deficiency, allied to the shortage of animal protein, explains why the children were usually thin and stunted and had a low haemoglobin content in the blood.

In consequence of the enquiry, milk products were introduced into the diets of two canteens, one in a day nursery and one in a school, where 700 children were fed. The results are convincing. It was not long before the children fed in these canteens were growing heavier and taller than the children who were eating in a control canteen into which milk products had not been introduced.

An investigation in Iran covered 92 families in Teheran and its suburbs, and also 62 families in the countryside around Azerbaijan. The families investigated belonged to varied social and economic classes, including small farmers, employees and land-owners. This investigation showed that the calorific content of the diet of small farmers was 20 per cent deficient; of employees, 4 per cent deficient; and of land-owners, more than 15 per cent deficient. In proteins, the deficiencies were 32 per cent, 28 per cent, and 19 per cent respectively; the deficiencies of animal protein being 73 per cent, 75 per cent and

38 per cent. Calcium and riboflavin were deficient by about 50 per cent.

Investigators found that food intake per person fell as size of family rose. This was true of families in every class and related most of all to foods of animal origin, these being the most expensive. The small farmers suffered most of all: among them, the large family (with three or more children) had 26 per cent fewer calories and 57 per cent less animal protein than the childless family. It is this which is to be blamed for the low state of health of the rural population. It partly explains the high infantile mortality rate (216·8 per thousand live births, four times as high as that of France) and the high rate of still-births (86·5 per thousand).

One of the facts of modern times is the acceleration of the growth of towns in all parts of the world. In 1850, there were in the whole world fewer than 100 towns with a population greater than 100,000: now, that number has multiplied more than tenfold. It is estimated that 12 per cent of the world's population live in the 700 largest cities in the world.

This rapid growth of towns is accompanied, in the under-developed regions, by a flight from the countryside which often reaches large proportions. It raises difficult social problems: and also, in the more backward countries, grave problems of nutrition. Where development of the countryside has not kept pace with urban growth there often ensues a lack of balance which shows itself in nutritional deficiencies of a more or less serious nature. As we have shown elsewhere,[12] villages in the interior in many of the under-developed countries still have a subsistence economy: that is to say, they sell little to and try to buy less from the outside world. Most African villages, as also many in Latin America and a part of Asia, are still at this stage of development.

On the other hand, the existing agrarian system and diffi-culties of transport due to the insufficiency of roads, bridges, railways, etc., will not always allow production to be increased to meet the new needs of the towns. At the same time, these countries are generally too poor to buy food from abroad to feed the urban population.

[12] Noël Drogat, *Pays sous-développées et coopération technique*, Part II, ch. 1: "De l'économie de subsistance à l'économie de marché", p. 107.

The situation varies, of course, from country to country according to the stage of economic development reached, the standard of living and the level of wages. Still, it seems to be established by the investigations which have been made into this matter[13] that the supply of food available to native town workers is largely dependent upon developments in the agricultural sector of these countries.

The evidence available indicates that in Africa it is the migrant workers who suffer the greatest fall in nutritional standards when they come to the town. In their villages they have been accustomed to grow most of what they need, and in town they find much difficulty in adapting themselves to their new environment. Their greatest difficulty is to realize that they must devote the greatest part of their wages to buy food which at home was to be had free.

It is among these workers that the greatest dietary deterioration is to be observed. An investigation into the eating habits of Bantus in the Union of South Africa has shown that they change for the worse from the moment the people come to live in the towns. The customary Bantu diet of unsieved cereals and milk is often changed for one based on sieved maize flour, white bread and mineral water. When they are at work the men eat badly, unless the company which employs them provides them with a substantial meal. An enquiry made by Dr C. H. Northcott into the conditions of 6,000 Africans employed at Nairobi by the Kenya-Uganda railway brings out the irregularity and frequent insufficiency of the men's meals.

> It often happens that the men eat very little in the morning and the lower paid among them have no midday meal. They go hungry over the greater part of the day and are apt to suffer from excessive weakness, giddiness, tiredness and irritability and to be unable to work well. Their calory intake is such that they cannot do heavy work.[14]

Even when a canteen is provided, it is not an easy task to persuade workers to take advantage of it: they would rather have money than the meal. There is an example of this from a

[13] U.N.: *Report on state of social affairs in the world*, 1957.

[14] U.N.E.S.C.O. *Social aspects of the industrialization and urbanization of Africa to the south of the Sahara*, p. 152.

factory in South Africa in which the management provided a well-balanced, subsidized meal, but where 90 per cent of the workers preferred to have the whole of their wages in money. Taking the advice of a doctor employed by the health service, the management engaged the services of a native teacher who was a specialist in problems of nutrition to explain to the work-people the nature of their needs. This he did, pointing out the difference in price and nutritional value between the canteen meal and the white bread and mineral water on which they were spending their wages. Within a month, 90 per cent of the workers were taking the canteen meal.[15] This example shows that it is not enough to put forward a rational proposal, but that it is equally important to make sure that what is being proposed is properly understood by the beneficiaries.

On the other hand, there are numerous examples which show the benefits to be derived from a well-appointed canteen in which African workers can buy food and other things at whole-sale prices.[16] At Brazzaville, the health of the workers has been appreciably improved since the opening of two canteens which serve substantial meals at low prices to the employees of two undertakings. The same is true of Duala, where four communal restaurants of this type have been opened in different parts of the port.

In some of the small African towns, the families of migrant workers are encouraged to grow food for themselves on allotments provided for them near the town. Quite often, they are able to raise some poultry and small livestock as well.

In Latin America, too, rapid growth of the towns has had much the same results as those we have described in Africa.

Between 1940 and 1951, the population of São Paulo in Brazil rose by 872,000 or 62 per cent. Three-quarters of this increase was due to the migration to the towns of the poverty-stricken people of the countryside. Brazil is a land of modern cities, but it has yet to bring much needed improvements to the lives of the mass of the countryfolk. Modernization of agriculture has hardly begun over the greater part of the country. Thus, to quote Tibor Mende:

[15] C.C.T.A. enquiry, *Les facteurs humains de la productivité en Afrique*, p. 16.
[16] U.N. Report on world social affairs.

Within a few hours flight of São Paulo or Rio de Janeiro, cosmopolitan cities to be compared with Paris or New York, naked savages shoot arrows against aircraft flying overhead, catch alligators, grow rice and jute in tiny clearings, or collect rubber from trees which grow wild in the jungle.

In Brazil, the flow of migration is mainly away from the poor and essentially rural states of the north and north-east towards those of the south and south-west, where the most important towns are situated and economic progress is most rapid. These migrant masses settle around the great cities, often in deplorable conditions of hygiene and housing, lacking purchasing power and finding it extremely difficult to feed themselves properly.

In the large towns there is a chronic shortage of perishable foodstuffs and even of some basic articles of diet. In addition to this, the distributive system is inefficient, costly and unsound. In some countries in Latin America the plantations and large estates are engaged in production for the export trade—coffee, cotton and sugar cane: while production for local consumption is carried on mainly by small-holders, whose output has not been increased fast enough to keep pace with the growth of the towns. These have, therefore, been compelled to depend to a large extent on imported products. Unless the small-holder himself takes his products to the town market—and whether he does this on foot or by cart there is a very great waste of time—the gap between the price which he will receive and the price which will be charged in the town will be generally excessive. Gathering, warehousing and transporting of perishables are all badly organized. Large quantities of such goods are lost through decay and vermin before they reach the town and by the time much of the rest is sold it is in a bad condition and even dangerous to eat.[17]

Governments try to rectify this state of affairs by imposing standards of hygiene on the market places and controlling the sale of certain products, but, since sales are so often made from door to door, these measures are of only limited value.

The poorer classes in the towns usually have a monotonous diet which is both badly balanced and insufficient. The wealthier

[17] U.N. Report on world social affairs.

families, there as everywhere else, are able to afford more meat, eggs, milk and other foods of high nutritional value (tinned and bottled goods included), and their consumption of these things rises faster than does their consumption of cereals and vegetables.

Just as in Africa, the public authorities and business undertakings organize canteens and communal restaurants which offer workers good meals at moderate prices.

Japan, which has been said to be the most remarkable testing ground for economic development in the whole world, certainly offers a particularly interesting example from the point of view of this book. There are some who believe that we can learn much from it about the future evolution of under-developed countries.

When the Japanese began the process of westernization, in 1868, the food production of the peasant was the equivalent of a half-ton of cereals: it is now more than quadrupled. One-third of output today consists of fish; fruit and vegetable cultivation have been greatly developed; and the output of rice has been more than doubled. This has been due to the modernization of the fisheries, the improvement of farm techniques and the use of fertilizers. While this growth of food production has been proceeding, more than half the population has moved into urban occupations and the general standard of living has been raised. Already, in the decade before the war, consumption per head of milk, meat, sugar, fats and tea increased in proportions varying between 13 and nearly 40 per cent.

Calory intake in the towns is slightly below that in the countryside, but it would appear that this difference merely reflects the more sedentary nature of town life and a smaller consumption of energy producing foods, such as cereals and potatoes. On the other hand, the consumption of foods rich in protein and other expensive articles of diet is higher in urban centres than in the countryside.

Investigations in other countries into questions of nutrition indicate the existence of similar tendencies.

The results of different enquiries made in India between 1935 and 1948 make it possible to compare the diets of different sections of the population there. One result that stands out is that the proportion of calories which is provided by fish, meat, fruits, vegetables, sugar and fats was, during that period, considerably higher for the industrial than for the agricultural worker.[18]

We have to be cautious in drawing conclusions from this evidence. Movement of people to the town is not necessarily accompanied by an improvement in their feeding. They may lack sufficient purchasing power; and as we have seen is happening in the African towns, their diets may even deteriorate, at least for as long as they lack permanent and better paid employment. It is in any case necessary not to neglect the modernization of the agricultural sector as the processes of urbanization and industrialization proceed.

[18] U.N. Report on world social affairs.

Part Two

The Conquest of Hunger

VI

THE SCOPE OF SCIENCE AND
TECHNICAL KNOWLEDGE

THE rapid growth of world population which is characteristic of the second half of the twentieth century is being
accompanied by technical and scientific advances in all
fields, including those of biology and agriculture. Fifty years
ago this advance was a bright prospect; today it has become a
reality. Men are in process of acquiring over nature a mastery
such as has never before been attained and which they can use
to eliminate the threat of hunger.

Progress already made in the study of soils, or pedology, and
also in genetics, animal management and botany, give us reason
to believe that present outputs can be easily increased. It is
obvious that progress in genetics is opening up a wonderful
prospect of growth and improvement in productivity. The
development of hybrid corn offers a striking example. Where
previously the yield was 15 quintals, it is now often 40 quintals
or more.

Antibiotics and synthetic insecticides are powerful weapons
against a number of pests. The study of trace elements has
demonstrated that the yield of some crops can be more than
doubled, even in some cases quadrupled, by the application of
relatively tiny doses of things like manganese, copper sulphate,
molybdenum, etc. Research into vernalization and photo-
periodicity also open up interesting possibilities and we are
beginning to see possible agricultural uses of radio-activity. It
would be safe to predict that the use of isotopes will become an
established part of agricultural techniques.[1]

[1] Prof. Pierre Chouard writes: "With this new atomic tool it becomes possible
to trace in detail the part played in the life of the cell by elements such as
phosphorus and potassium; and it is likely that the incomparably more precise
knowledge which this research will give us on the way in which fertilizers work
will lead to the development of new techniques for using them."

In the opinion of many scholars today, the time is not far distant when men will have discovered the secrets of photosynthesis and will be able to use the inexhaustible reserves of solar energy to improve the feeding of mankind. Progress is being made in finding ways to use arid and semi-arid regions and it is already possible to grow some plants in the polar regions. All over the world research is going on and promising results have already been obtained. In the very near future, perhaps, atomic bombs will be used to transform the salt "lakes" of Tunisia and the Sahara into an inland sea.

It is the opinion of the experts at the F.A.O., who are aware of the possibilities opened up by modern agricultural techniques, that in making these available on a large scale to the under-developed countries our generation will succeed in eradicating hunger from the world. In a recent booklet, designed to popularize plans for agricultural action which would be adapted to the needs of these countries, the F.A.O. has this to say:

> The application of proved scientific techniques to the less advanced agricultural economies would make possible a rate of growth of output which is greater than is now taking place and much greater than the rate of growth of population. Land and water can be used much more effectively than they are at present so as to increase all crop yields substantially as well as to raise productivity in cattle rearing, fishing and forestry.[2]

Thanks to the new methods, there are very good prospects of improved crop yields in the under-developed countries, which for the most part are still using primitive techniques. The general expectation is that present yields can be doubled or even trebled. This means that if modern methods were employed, there would be a more than adequate supply of food in those countries.

There are well established methods for making cultivation more intensive, among them being the use of selected seeds and the appropriate methods of culture to keep the soil clean and friable. If to these techniques are added certain basic principles of farm management, the most important of these

[2] *Choice of projects for national action*, F.A.O., 1960.

being the rational use of water, results can be spectacular. A well designed irrigation network sometimes enables farmers to increase their outputs tenfold, and a good system of land drainage can lead to appreciably larger yields.

It has been shown by experience that it is relatively easy and cheap to get farmers to use improved strains of selected seeds. It is one of the most successful and economically least burdensome methods of both qualitatively and quantitatively improving food production. Numerous cases have shown that it is possible in this way to obtain very quick results. In 1957, when the F.A.O. launched its "world seed campaign", high yielding Italian wheat was introduced into Yugoslavia. In two years production had increased by 30 per cent and a country which formerly had to import more than 5,000,000 quintals of wheat each year was able to provide for its own needs for the first time in its history. In Iran, where home grown cotton supplies an important textile industry, F.A.O. experts helped in the introduction of improved varieties which both in yield and in quality were far superior to the strains previously used. A scheme for the distribution of the seeds was set on foot and a national committee is now engaged in organizing the production, testing and distribution of pure cotton seed.

It is perhaps with rice that it is most important to popularize the best varieties and the best methods of cultivation. Even today, rice is still almost the only food for 54 per cent of the world's population. In the whole of South-east and a large part of Eastern Asia, rice growing is one of the most important farm employments. At the present time, it is Japan which is the most successful rice growing country in the whole of the Far East, thanks to the widespread employment there of better strains and to the attention paid to every aspect of rice cultivation, and particularly to the maintenance and improvement of the fertility of the soil.

It is the opinion of specialists that in most tropical countries rice growers do not make proper use of manures by carefully balancing organic material with chemical nitrogenous fertilizers, such as sulphate of ammonia. Often also, insufficient attention is given to weeding.[3] A striking contrast between two countries situated in the same latitude is provided by Formosa and the

[3] K. Ramiah, *Factors influencing rice production*, F.A.O., 1955.

Indian state of Uttar Pradesh. Yields in Formosa are twice as large as those in Uttar Pradesh, because the Formosans practise intensive cultivation with the use of manure.

In India, rice is grown on more than 12,000,000 acres and for some years now efforts have been made to adapt Japanese methods to Indian conditions. A campaign has been under way to increase food production in most of the Indian rice-growing states, an essential part of it being the production and distribution of selected seed. The first results show an increase in output of nearly half a ton to the acre and there is hope of raising rice output within ten or fifteen years by some 40–50,000,000 tons. States such as Madras and Bombay are ahead of others in this work, and the former reports that nearly half the acreage under rice is planted with the improved varieties.

Four years has been a long enough period for Egypt to produce and distribute to its farmers the seed of an improved strain of rice. More than 85 per cent of the rice acreage is of this variety and output has been almost doubled. Similar steps have been taken in other countries, notably in Ceylon, Indonesia, Thailand and the Philippines, but it will take some years of effort before these countries overtake Japan.

The preference for rice which exists in all eastern and far eastern countries is due to its exceptional qualities.

> The explanation for the primacy of rice is to be found above all in the fact that it is an irrigated plant: this guarantees higher yields from it than can be got from any other cereal grown in the same soil. Thanks to the fact that it is pricked out, its cultivation calls for less seed and it occupies the land for a relatively short period, thereby enabling several harvests to be gathered from the same plot. Rice suffers less than other cereals from either a dearth or an excess of water. The paddy (unmilled rice grain) keeps well and is less subject than maize to attack by weevils.[4]

Maintenance of soil fertility is nowadays an imperative duty. Until now, men have been able to dispose of new continents, but that phase is now ended. Henceforth, they must learn to use the land everywhere and behave towards it as would a good father to his family.

[4] Auguste Chevalier, *L'agriculture coloniale*, p. 88.

This is a matter of capital importance for the future of humanity. In a world which is threatened with famine, methods of farming which "mine" the land, and which were and are still practised in some countries, constitute an attack on a collective inheritance of fundamental importance. In the early stage of American colonization, it was said by Jefferson that it cost less to buy an acre of new land than to manure an acre of old land. This manner of acting, which has not been confined to the U.S.A., has led to much squandering of arable land.

Almost fifty years ago, the alarm was given by the Americans themselves. It is well known how strongly the U.S.A. acted and what effort it put into a campaign to arouse popular action against this disastrous state of affairs. Many countries have followed the American example and have established special services to combat erosion and deterioration of the soil. Latin America, too, has sensed the danger as its population has increased. In China, where the floods of the Yellow and the Blue Rivers often reach catastrophic dimensions, immense works have been undertaken to dam and embank these dangerous rivers. India is doing likewise with the Ganges and the Indus.

The Marcial Valley, in Haiti, presents a typical example of the damage done to farming by failure to control water.

> Year after year, the Gosseline, swollen by the tropical rains, tears away from the valley thousands of tons of good earth and spills it into the sea. The soil crumbles away under the sun and loses its humus. It is estimated that 15 per cent of the land has been made infertile by erosion; while 70 per cent has lost a large part of its fertility and needs protection urgently.[5]

There are 30,000 poor farmers living in that valley who are alternately reduced to famine by prolonged droughts or floods when the Gosseline is in spate.

The problem is, indeed, enormous. There are many parts of Africa, of India and of South America where the soil is used only occasionally. Herdsmen look for new pasturage and agriculturalists move around, building new villages and cultivating new lands. Often, when they move, they burn the new lands to

[5] U.N.E.S.C.O., *Experiment in Haiti*.

C.H.—7

get a fresh growth of more succulent grass or to clear the forest. These primitive methods have grave disadvantages and attempts are now being made to find a remedy. It is known that bush fires lead to a rapid deterioration of the soil in savannah country: there is a hardening of the subsoil, rich in iron, and its composition is altered irreversibly. The land becomes as hard as brick and the thin covering of sandy soil is quickly eroded away.

F.A.O. experts who have made a special study of this problem in Africa insist on the seriousness of it.

It is extremely important, wherever it can be done, to prevent the savannah from overspreading the fallow land and care must be taken always not to burn it, since the fire would have bad effects on the soil itself and destroy its qualities. Protection against fire would encourage the return of soil regenerating forest to enormous areas of savannah, the growth of which is largely due to human action, and many acres of soil would again become productive through deliberate use of forest clearings.[6]

It is more necessary in tropical areas than it is elsewhere to protect the soil from being washed out by the rains and to allow the periodical restoration of humus.

In other regions, wind-breaks of trees can be planted to protect the soil from dry winds, or, where the danger comes from topsoil being washed downhill, terrace cultivation or contour ploughing should be used. Where nomadic agriculture is still practised in the Near and Middle East, measures are in hand to prevent herds of goats, sheep and other animals from over-grazing and utterly exhausting the soil. Use of shelters and enclosures for cattle, as also regulation of pasture—a delicate undertaking—by agreement with the users of it, are recommended measures to remedy the situation.

[6] F.A.O. *Soil Conservation*, p. 144. In this system, large clearings or corridors would be made in the forest, each clearing being some ½ mile to 1¼ miles long and 300 yards wide. A corridor would be brought under cultivation in the years when the trees had been cut down and the land allowed to rest from tree growing, in such a way that every cultivated clearing would be surrounded by trees. After the undergrowth has been burned, the larger wood being allowed to rot down to help to provide organic matter to the soil, maize, rice, cassava and plantains are sown or planted.

In some cases, it may be found better to stop farming the land and replant trees, while cultivation of grass and animal forage can sometimes be used instead of forest to retain rain water in the soil and to protect it against erosion. The American National Resources Board states that erosion is sixty-five times greater on cultivated soil than it is on grassland with the same slope, and in addition grassland holds five times more water.

After having spent some time in India studying the question, M. René Dumont recently set down what seemed to him to be the priorities to be observed to obtain better results in that country. He was impressed with the need to pay special attention to soil conditions.

Next to the problem of water, the most essential matter concerns the conservation of the soil. Many other questions are intimately bound up with this problem. It is obviously necessary to encourage greater use of fertilizers and to increase production of them, but it is green manuring which will play a predominant role in improving soil structures. Green manures ought to be undersown. Some varieties of them (*crotalaria striata*, for example) can supply woody stems for fuel as well as matter for ploughing in. Where tree planting is also undertaken, use of cow-dung for fuel can be reduced. Animal fodder and wood are closely allied problems.[7]

Another approach to the problem of increasing food output is to grow more of the foods which give a high yield of calories to the acre, care being taken to preserve a balance both in diets and in soil fertility.

Calory value varies much from crop to crop: an acre of wheat, for example, gives many more calories than does an acre of grass. Basing their figures on the results of a number of experiments carried out in America, technical men there have drawn up the following table of calories to the acre: potatoes, 2,850,000; wheat, 1,350,000; pig rearing, 625,000; dairy farming, 440,000; cattle rearing on pasture, 56,000.[8]

[7] René Dumont, *Économie rurale*, July–Sept. 1959.

[8] According to M. Sapper, the highest yields of calories to the acre are obtained from sugar, both of cane and beet. Next come the starchy foods and tubers—bananas, cassava, potatoes. Cereals—rice and wheat—come next. Animal products come a long way down the scale, but it must be borne in mind that they have an important effect on the preservation of health. (*L'Alimentation de l'Humanité*.)

It is understandable that some countries should meet the challenge of feeding a larger population by concentrating farm outputs more on crops, such as roots and starchy tubers, which have a high yield of calories to the acre. This process is often made easier by conditions of climate and soil which make cattle rearing and cereal growing more difficult. The result is a fall in the production of foods which are richer in protein, whether vegetable or animal, and this is not without danger for the health of populations never far removed from the various forms of malnutrition due to protein deficiency.

SUGAR 10·1

BANANAS 5·6

CASSAVA 4·8

POTATOES 4·7

RICE 2·7

| WHEAT | 2.1 (cultivated intensively) |

MILK 0·7

MEAT 0·16

Average Calory Yield
(millions to the acre)

This is particularly true of the cultivation of cassava in tropical regions. The tuberous roots of this plant are for the inhabitants of these warm areas what the potato is for the peoples in temperate climates. It is easy to cultivate, yields abundantly and has only to be pulled out of the ground when it is needed. On the other hand, it contains but little protein and fats and so is a food of no very great nutritive value; and in addition to this, in some varieties of it there is a toxic element which can only be removed by putting the sliced tubers to soak in water.

A plant which is so easy to grow suits the peoples of the tropical forest admirably. The laziest man has only to stick a fragment of cassava stalk in the soil to be able to gather without any further effort a product which is certainly poor enough, but which could not be less well suited to the idleness of the cultivator. Diets which are based exclusively on cassava and plantains are necessarily gravely defective, however great the quantity of food which may be eaten.

In tropical countries, where milk and meat are rarely eaten, it would seem to be necessary to improve the balance of domestically grown foodstuffs by the introduction of leguminous plants which are quite rich in proteins, such as tropical varieties of beans, peas and ground nuts. Most of these leguminous plants have a high nutritive value, but only the ground nut is cultivated on a large scale. It would be worth while to increase their cultivation, as is suggested in the F.A.O. publication on the choice of projects for national action.

The introduction into the established economy of underdeveloped countries of crops grown for the market has often hastened the evolution we have just described, leading to a decline in domestic food production and having other quite destructive consequences. As the geographer Pierre Georges has noted: "The immediate consequence is a breakdown in the delicate balance of the traditional dietary regime. In the longer run, overcropping leads to soil exhaustion and to crop yields becoming inferior to those obtained on plantations."[9]

Striking instances have been given by René Dumont in the monographs which he has written on Negro Africa, while Pierre Gourou cites Brazil as an example of a country where the harmful consequences of imprudent methods of cultivation for the market are evident.[10] We have to recognize that we are still far away from having the answer to this problem. Questions which call for our most serious attention today concern the best use of soils, crop specialization, schemes of rotation best fitted to maintain or to restore the fertility of the soil, matters which, in the under-developed countries today, are essential to a progressive agriculture which must become more and more intensive.

---

[9] Pierre Georges, *La campagne: le fait rurale à travers le monde* (1956).

[10] René Dumont, *L'Économie agricole dans le monde* (1953): Pierre Gourou, *Les Pays tropicaux* (1953).

The general rule should be to practise mixed farming wherever conditions allow, plants and animals together making possible a better biological balance in the soil. In this sphere there is a vast field for research open to agronomists who are anxious to find the best solutions for the needs of every part of the world.

Under-developed countries suffer much more than do others from spoilage of crops by insects and other depredators. Marx Sorre has remarked that "in the scheme of nature, every individual being brings with him a retinue of living creatures which live at his expense" and that, in the last resort, man harvests only what the parasites choose to leave for him. This is exactly what happens in those countries.

Some of these parasites are particularly destructive. Locusts, for example, can eat up the crops of an entire region. They breed extremely rapidly, the female laying up to 20,000 eggs in one square yard of soil. They swarm in immense clouds which can travel for thousands of miles at a rate of around forty miles a day. Wherever they settle, nothing escapes. The greatest locust clouds can be 50 miles wide and just as long. The locusts were one of the plagues of Egypt in biblical times and to this day they present an ever present threat of disaster for the countries of the Near East and of Northern Africa.

An anti-locust campaign is difficult to conduct because it far outruns the capacity of any one country. Their breeding grounds extend over a large part of the African continent and across the South-west of Asia as far as India. We are still badly informed on the areas and conditions in which they breed. All that we do know is that they require certain types of vegetation, and that breeding depends also on the nature of the soil, the conformation of the ground and atmospheric conditions.

In the face of a task of this size, international organizations under the aegis of U.N.E.S.C.O. and with the help of experts from F.A.O. have set on foot, in the last few years, a general plan which disposes of resources greater than national anti-locust campaigns can obtain. This will allow of field research on a large scale and the use of very powerful weapons in the struggle, such as aircraft to attack swarms in flight or after they have settled on the ground.

First attention has been given to the southern side of the Red Sea, where the locust breeds during the winter, and to

Central Arabia, where it breeds in springtime. Instructional courses in anti-locust methods are now organized at Bikanir in India, Malik in Pakistan, Asmara in Ethiopia, Dakar in Senegal, and in Mauritania.[11]

Africa has other pests which can do almost as much damage, in their own way, as does the locust. One such is the weaver-bird. This is a pretty bird, with a red beak, black neck and beige plumage. It nests in the jungle, in bushes and in marsh-land, forming colonies which number in millions. There can be as many as 2,000 nests in one tree. It is often difficult to get at the laying grounds because the birds quite readily build their nests in pools and weapons to combat them have to be carried in dinghies or motor boats. In the Sudan and in Senegal the army and the air force have been called upon to deal with the innumerable flocks which come down every year upon the corn fields, eating and destroying all the crop. Recently, one campaign which was really heavily mounted has succeeded in destroying more than 30,000,000 eggs and reducing the weaver-bird population by 90 per cent.

Losses due to imperfection in the products or, as is often the case, lack of proper storage for cereals and the fruits of leguminous crops also reduce the availability of food resources in the poorer countries. It is estimated that rats, insects and fungi spoil about one-third of every harvest. This alone can be the cause of undernourishment for 30 per cent of the population.

Governments have now had their attention drawn to the importance of this problem and several have sought the aid of F.A.O. in finding solutions to it. An international expert has established storage and handling systems in Burma which have reduced rice losses by from 40 to 50 per cent. In the same way, handling and processing of dates have been improved in Libya, Iraq and Saudi Arabia.

In Iraq, it was a question of action on a commercial scale, with the installation of a modern factory to handle about 300,000 tons of dates a year for export, so as to meet the requirements of world markets. Using modern machinery and well-trained personnel, this experimental factory has a daily output of 100 tons of boxed dates at costs which are well below those of the older methods. At the same time, a laboratory has

[11]U.N.E.S.C.O., *The arid zones.*

been established to study the industrial processing and use of waste products to feed cattle and in other ways. Iraq now has one of the best date preparing installations in existence and, being able to supply dates of a high quality, has been able greatly to expand its markets. F.A.O. has equipped another factory in Libya to provide for the needs of local consumption and plans another to produce dates to feed the school population.

Foodstuffs which have been preserved by the traditional methods—drying in the sun, smoking, salting, pickling, sterilization by heating, fermentation, etc.—play an important part in the diets of numerous countries. But these are small-scale methods, worked out empirically over the course of centuries, and they can be greatly improved by the application to them of modern methods of food technology. It is in this way that new ways of drying fish have of late years been tried out in Africa.

In the great majority of cases, and certainly with peasant peoples who have remained at a subsistence level, it is necessary to make use of simple means of storing and processing products, using improved equipment which calls for as little of what cannot be found locally as is possible. Where there are large city populations to be fed, the position is different: in such cases it will often be proper to consider the use of modern storage facilities, like grain silos and refrigeration plants for perishables like meat, fish, fruit, milk and eggs.[12]

Refrigeration is now an important industry which has done much to change our eating habits. It is thanks to it that tropical fruits which are so easily spoiled can be stored and transported without loss. An example is afforded by the banana trade, which is now perfected. We can expect that in the future, and on a much larger scale, it will be possible for continent to trade with continent, each allowing the others to benefit from its own particular products.

There are also possibilities of extending the area of cultivable land. For some years now, a group of experts drawn from many countries have worked together, under the aegis of

---

[12] In the Middle and Far East, an animal must be eaten immediately it has been slaughtered, for meat cannot be preserved. This explains the custom for each family in turn to kill an animal, a sheep or a pig, and invite the neighbours to a feast.

U.N.E.S.C.O., to make a particular study of the arid and semi-arid zones which cover more than a third of the earth's land surface. By contrast, cultivated lands cover no more than a tenth. For every acre of cultivated land there are three or four acres which are virtually unusable—deserts or semi-desert covered with a sparse vegetation which can do no more than support a most precarious subsistence economy, such as that which is practised by the nomadic peoples. Hence the importance of the U.N. major project for research into the arid zones which was set on foot in 1957.

The study of how to make these lands useful raised numerous problems which call upon the resources of various fields of study—geology, hydrology, climatology, botany, and also sociology, for means must be found to meet the needs of the peoples who wander across these immense and almost empty spaces. But the essential point is to discover how to increase supplies of water with which to bring life to these desolate lands.[13]

What has been done by the U.S.S.R. in the arid regions of Central Asia and the Transcaucasus shows that important results can be obtained. In Southern Siberia, the construction of a large dam on the Sir-Daria River and a reservoir at Kair-kum is expected to provide for the irrigation of 750,000 acres of virgin soil. In the next few years the collective farms in these regions are to bring all this land under cultivation. An immense expanse of water has been created in the heart of the celebrated Karakoram by means of a canal which has been cut right across Southern Turkmenistan, from the Amu-Darya to the foothills of the Kopet-Dag. This canal will provide for the irrigation of several millions of acres. In Azerbaijan, the Apcheron canal has been completed and water is led to the irrigated lands in asbestos cement pipes which are more than 600 miles long.

In a report to U.N.E.S.C.O., Professor Bogomolov, who has specialized in these matters, gave the following details:

[13] At a U.N.E.S.C.O. discussion on arid zones, held in May, 1960, this question of water utilization was debated at length. It emerged from the discussion that there is no one universal solution, but a great number of answers of different types, such as the harnessing of subterranean supplies, large and small dams and reservoirs, among which it is necessary to choose those which best meet the needs of a country and its people.

Taking into account the great irrigation works in the Ukraine, in Northern Caucasus and in the republics of Transcaucasia and Kazakhstan, within the next few years the area of irrigated land in the U.S.S.R. will be reckoned in tens of millions of acres. These works are truly transforming nature: river courses are being changed, lands irrigated, forests reestablished so as to improve the climate, retain water and protect the land from dry winds, control the run-off of surface water, lessen soil erosion and render rivers more navigable. The map of the Soviet Union is being changed and deserts are beginning to disappear.[14]

Much research had to be undertaken to make these great works possible and geological, climatic, soil composition and other maps had to be prepared to give the information without which the plans could not have been carried through.

Analogous researches are being undertaken in West Pakistan with a view to the recovery of the arid zone of Baluchistan. The work is being directed by the Geophysical Institute in Quetta, founded in 1951 with the help of U.N.E.S.C.O. It is estimated that about one-third of Baluchistan can be made available for grazing, and 12 per cent (100,000,000 acres) can be brought under cultivation by means of a better utilization of water. At the present time only 37,000,000 acres are being put to any use and only 20 per cent of those are normally cultivated in the course of a year. The region is not entirely without water, since there are twelve streams which have their sources in Baluchistan, among them being the Zhob, which flows into the Indus. Experiments with rotor driven wind pumps 18 feet in diameter have shown that it is possible to draw water from a depth of 100 feet at a rate of from 1,000 to 4,750 gallons a day. These wind-pumps should be enough to provide the villages with water, irrigate the small gardens and water the flocks on the grazing grounds. Near the mouth of the Hab River there is a market garden area which supplies the Karachi market: there, judiciously spaced wind pumps are able each to irrigate about $6\frac{1}{4}$ acres with an inch of water a day.[15]

[14] G. V. Bogomolov, "Research and cultivation in the arid and semi-arid regions of U.S.S.R." in *Arid Zones* (U.N.E.S.C.O., June, 1959).

[15] H. I. S. Tirlaway, "Results of research at the Geophysical Institute of Quetta into problems of arid zones": *Arid Zones*, June, 1959.

The results which have been obtained in the state of Israel are the best known. They illustrate in a remarkable way how it is possible to transform desert into cultivated land through proper soil management and the use of water. In that area, where water has been insufficient in summer and all too plentiful in winter, dams have been built to control the streams and prevent them from becoming torrents. Unhealthy regions have been made healthy, particularly by the draining of Lake Hula, and transformed into fertile farmlands. An artificial lake 2,500 acres in extent is being formed in the heart of Galilee. Thanks largely to the work of Professor Michael Evanari, the desert of the Negev in the south is retreating and giving place to fields of ground nuts, olive trees, pomegranates, apricots, vines and even cereals. Use has been made again of techniques used in former times in the area—terraced fields and irrigation by means of trickling streams.

In the space of ten years, Israel has recovered 300,000 acres of arid land and 1,300,000,000 cubic yards of water is stored annually to irrigate them. Herds of live-stock have been tripled. A growing population is self-supporting in vegetables, fruits, milk, eggs and poultry, while agricultural exports are worth more than £1,000,000 a year.

Results which have been achieved in the Sahara are also widely known. Drilling which has been done in the search for oil has confirmed the presence at a considerable depth of water which can be raised by means of artesian wells or by pumping. Wells giving a large flow have been sunk. The artesian well at Ouargla gives 40,000 cubic yards of water a day from a depth of 3,000 feet. One of the latest drillings, at Hobba, close to El Oued, yields 13,000 cubic yards of water a day and irrigates 500 acres of palms and farm land. Recently, there has been success at Sidi Mahdi, where water is brought up from a depth of nearly 5,000 feet at the rate of 5,000 gallons a minute. This will allow the creation of an irrigated area of about 2,500 acres, 900 of which will be devoted to date palms and other fruit trees and 1,600 to cereals and fodder crops.

Since 1958, people living in the Sahara have been able to eat fresh vegetables, not brought in by air but provided by the research station at Beni Abbas. This station, which was planned by Professor Pierre Chouard, grows magnificent salads, cabbages, radishes and tomatoes in the sand and in the full glare of the sun, without any shade. Maize, castor-oil plants and ground nuts have also been grown. The method used is to build cement tanks about five yards long and one yard wide, and make them impervious by means of a thin film of plastic material. At the bottom of the tanks is laid a gravel bed about one inch deep and over that is placed a bed of sand about five inches deep. Plant foods—mineral salts, sulphate of magnesia and trace elements—are injected into the sand through perforated plastic tubes, which have the advantage of using much less water than would a system of spraying. It costs less to grow the crops than to bring them in by air from France, but the technique calls for competent people who are able to make up the correct prescriptions of feeding solutions and to deal with the parasites which have not been slow to arrive.

There is talk even of creating an inland sea in the Sahara. The plan is by no means a new one, but it has been lately (1957) taken up again by A.R.T.E.M.I.S.[16] It would be necessary to cut through the Gabes Isthmus and the Tozeur and Asloudje passes, as well as to build a canal to the north of the Shott Djerid. It is estimated that there would be five or six times as much earth to move as was the case with the Suez canal, but today the task would be much facilitated by the use of thermonuclear explosions. One 20 megaton charge (in TNT equivalent) would blow a crater 4,000 yards in diameter. The cost would be of the order of £80,000,000.

This project would bring many advantages. It would allow ocean-going vessels to sail right into the Sahara region, which would greatly assist the exploitation of its mineral resources. Pressure of the sea-water would raise [the level of the subterranean reserves of fresh water which supply the oases in this region. People dwelling along the shores would be able to establish a fishing industry. There would also be a general increase in fertility, since rainfall would be greatly increased by the intense evaporation from the surface of the sea.

At the other extreme of climate, the Russians are busy bringing into use the polar regions in the north of Siberia. Industrial centres have been established on rich mineral deposits

[16] Association for technical research into the problems of creating an inland Saharan Sea.

there and the growing towns have to be fed. Since means of transport are still scanty and the distances are enormous, it has been necessary to seek for ways of growing food locally. Although the summer is very short, lasting only 70 to 90 days, the Russian specialists have been able to grow vegetables, potatoes, some fruits and even cereals by means of a technique called vernalization.[17]

New strains of potatoes which have been developed at the plant breeding centre of Kirovak, on the Kola Peninsula, are being grown in the neighbourhood of Obdorsk, a town of more than 100,000 inhabitants. The same centre has developed a strain of oats which ripens in ten weeks. The veterinary station at Obdorsk itself has specialized in the raising of reindeer and has introduced a type of cattle from Greenland. This is the musk ox, an animal of remarkable qualities which provides milk, meat and wool.[18]

On the Yenisei River, near the town of Igarka, is the polar plant breeding station of Polyarni. Here new strains of tubers and cereals are developed. The yield of the kohlrabi there is sometimes as high as 200 quintals to the acre. "The swamps about the town have been drained. Where the thaw used to bring floods (and the frost is permanent $2\frac{1}{2}$ to 3 inches down), there are now to be seen market gardens and fields of corn. High grade dairy cows are raised there, all that is needed to feed them being provided from the locality." The place is an important centre of the timber trade and a factory has been built there to extract glucose from the waste wood. This is used to feed cattle.[19]

[17] Vernalization is a technique worked out by the Russian biologist Lysenko. The seed is germinated artificially, then at a certain stage of development the germinating process is stopped, and afterwards the seed is sown in the ordinary way. The technique has the advantage of shortening the growing period and of providing a more precocious plant, a matter which is of the utmost importance in cold climates.

[18] The musk ox "needs no stable nor does it need to be fed. It finds its food under many feet of snow and, more important, builds up large reserves in summer. By the autumn, a male of 650 to 900 lbs will have accumulated a store of about 100 lbs of fat about its neck. . . . We were shown samples of a wool, very light yellow in colour and with a silky feel. This wool sprouts at the root of what looks like horse-hair." (Anton Zischka, *L'Asie qui se fait*, p. 201.)

[19] "Potatoes are ground and dried and mixed with the sugar which has been extracted from the wood. This is good fodder and will keep indefinitely. The farms around Igarka even supply butter to the towns of Dudinka and Norilsk. Provision is being made for the feeding of an ever growing population which, for its part, is allowing an expansion of the timber industry." (Ibid. pp. 285-6.)

Everyone knows that animal products are expensive. Land which is used for animal pasture has the lowest calory yield of any. It has been calculated that whereas one acre of potatoes will feed four men and of cereals, two or three men, one acre of meadow land will nourish scarcely one man.

It is best therefore to dispense with the intermediary steps of the meadow and the cow, where means of support are scarce, and make sure that man himself is fed, for the greater part of what the animal eats is used to maintain itself in being. Inhabitants of the Far East are well aware of this: to them, meat eating is wasteful, not to be indulged in except on festive days. As the Chinese peasant said to the European when the latter expressed his astonishment at not finding any cattle rearing: "If you give a cabbage to a beast and then eat the meat, you lose three-quarters of the nutritional value which you could have got by eating the cabbage yourself." Long before scientists had discovered the reasons for this, the Chinese knew it and put their knowledge into practice.[20]

On the other hand, let us quote this pleasing remark of the Japanese traveller, visiting France for the first time and seeing herds of cows almost everywhere grazing freely in large meadows: "How odd! Gardens for cows! When we do have cows, at home, they are kept in the byres." Soil is scarce in Japan and is put to its maximum use. Through force of circumstances some countries find it worth while to obtain the neces-

[20] To solve the world's problems of an insufficiency of foodstuffs, there are some who have put forward the suggestion that mankind adopt a vegetarian diet. In view of the important part which animal protein plays in the preservation of health, this proposal seems to be a last resource. In fact, it does not have the advantages which are ascribed to it, for animals are fed to no inconsiderable degree on by-products which are unsuitable for human consumption—bran, cattle cake, beetroot tops, brewery wastes, etc. It must also be borne in mind that animal wastes are important for the maintenance of soil fertility.

In addition to all this, the evidence of statistics is that "out of a total production of some 450,000,000 tons of cereals which can be used for bread-making (mainly wheat and rice), only 3 per cent is devoted to animal feeding and could be diverted to human consumption. As regards secondary cereals, at first sight the position appears to offer greater possibilities given that 40 per cent of these are used for animal feeding. However, 90 per cent of these quantities are used in North America and Europe". It can hardly be imagined that these countries would be willing to reverse a trend which is now more than a hundred years old and revert to an essentially vegetarian diet. (See the account given by N. Wright, Assistant Director General of F.A.O., to the British Association meeting in 1960: "The Answer to the Problems of World Feeding.")

sary protein from more economical sources than butchers' meat.

There is another factor operating in tropical regions: climatic conditions make cattle rearing more difficult and subject it to risks which can take a heavy toll of herds. The uncertainty of the rains, in particular, can be a sore trial for cattle, which may be forced through a dry season lasting as long as six or seven months to search for grass which is both scanty and poor. In the tropical savannah lands, most of the grasses become tough and are deficient in phosphorous, an essential element for growth in cattle.

A first consequence of the poverty of tropical grasslands is the slow growth of the animals. A Malagasy beast takes six or seven years to reach maturity. In addition, the cattle need immense areas: it is estimated that tropical pasture can support only 25 pounds of live weight to the acre, against 250 in Europe.[21]

Then there are the parasites and the high temperatures which further try the animals. In Central Africa, the areas which are infested with tsetse fly are practically unusable for cattle rearing. Over large areas it has been found necessary to clear away undergrowth in an effort to get rid of this pest, which works havoc on cattle. In the monsoon zone of tropical Asia, on the other hand, the violent rains can so chill cattle, particularly young animals, as to cause their death.

Finally, a tropical climate is unfavourable for the preservation of animal products—milk, butter, cheese and meat. It is only in the moist regions of some high plateaux that conditions are to be found which are favourable to meat and dairy production. Indeed, there are places where it is possible to take a grass crop every eight weeks and use it to feed dairy cattle, which are better kept in their byres. "Milk yields of cows which have been protected from the tropical sun are much higher, but many farmers are unaware of this. They even hesitate to cultivate meadows because they do not know that hay can be used to get milk."[22] In semi-arid regions, there is usually no attempt made to gather fodder at the growing period and

[21] Pierre Gourou, *Les pays tropicaux*, p. 63.
[22] Report of F.A.O.-W.H.O. Joint Committee, 1953.

conserve it to provide feeding for cattle throughout the year. Often, the grass is simply burnt.

Until quite recently, the African or Malagasy herdsman thought of his cattle as a symbol of his wealth and a means of exchange. Hence, there was an established custom—not a religious taboo, as in India—not to eat meat. This is what has been called "sentimental cattle-rearing". It can lead to absurd situations, such as this reported by René Dumont. Questioning a native chief about a mountainous pile of unutilized manure, he received this reply. "I am an old man and will soon die. When the passers-by see this mound they will think of me and say: 'There was a great chief, for he had a large herd.'" The reporter adds: "The possible use of fertilizer as a memorial had till then escaped me."

In spite of the difficulties which cattle rearing meets with in some areas, F.A.O. experts are of the opinion that

> it would be easy to double the actual numbers of sheep and cattle if deeper study were made of tropical and subtropical pasture land, if knowledge we already have on how to maintain and improve pasture land were generally applied, and if the yields of cereal and fodder crops for animals were raised. The rearing of pigs and poultry can be developed without much difficulty, provided that we increase the output of animal feeding stuffs and make better use of waste and by-products.[23]

Several countries which would like to increase or to improve their cattle population are beginning to be interested in schemes for the intensification of fodder production which call for a rational exploitation of pasture land and, in particular, for the inclusion of grass and pulse crops in the rotation plan. Aided by F.A.O. experts, the Indian government has already made considerable efforts to improve its pasture lands and to develop the cultivation of fodder crops. Similar action is being taken in Syria and Libya, where attempts are being made to improve the nomadic pastures by shutting areas off from grazing for a period so as to give them time to recover.

Cereals have priority in the countries around the Mediterranean and in the Near East. There, René Dumont thinks that

[23] F.A.O., *Agriculture in the world economy*, p. 41.

much can be done to develop cattle rearing and the growth of fodder crops which are adapted to climate and soil.

The example of Israel shows us that a rotation of fodder crops and a development of intensive cattle rearing afford the surest means to an increase in the production of animal foodstuffs and animal energy side by side with that of the yields of grain. The greatest production of fodder is to be got from the carob or locust tree. In this climate, but grown in deep soil from selected strains in Cyprus, the yield can reach 24 to 28 quintals of dried carobs to the acre from plantations which have been established for 12 or 15 years. Grown in irrigated ground in Israel, the crop can yield 70 quintals to the acre.[24]

Then there is the water.

When they are considering the possible food resources of this planet, people often take too little account of what the oceans and inland waters can provide.

Three quarters of the earth's surface is covered by sea and the biological wealth which it contains, and of which we still do not know enough, is immense. Life teems in the ocean, which is an enormous protein factory. As Professor Mrak, President of the University of California, has remarked, we are still at a prehistoric stage in this field: "Fishermen today are to be compared to the nomadic hunters who made irremediable inroads into the animal wealth of the globe. We have now to move from the hunting stage to that of settled and rational fish raising."

To make fishing really profitable we need to have a great deal of information which is not ordinarily within the reach of the solitary enquirer. The development of the science of oceanography calls for special equipment and the collaboration of different countries. That is why U.N.E.S.C.O. called a special conference in Copenhagen, in 1960, to consider the measures needed to facilitate international oceanographic research: the application of an international research programme, the training of specialists in oceanography and the availability of international oceanographic research vessels.

[24] R. Dumont, *Revue d'économie rurale* (1958).

In the course of the last few years, research has been carried on at many places and notably in the Indian Ocean. These have furnished proof that there is much more fish in the sea than had been supposed and that, subject to certain conditions, this supply can be increased. It has been demonstrated by the Wood Hole Oceanographic Institution, for example, that exploitation of ocean levels below those usually fished would increase the world catch by about 30,000,000 tons. Similarly, more rational utilization of plant and animal plankton, which is the ordinary food of sea fauna, would make possible a notable increase in the supply of fish. On a narrow arm of the sea enclosed by barrages at the marine research station at Millport, Dr F. Gross has made experiments which have given convincing results.

650 pounds of nitrates and 250 pounds of superphosphates were poured into three acres of water. The stimulus given to the plankton was immense: from 2,000 organisms to the cubic centimetre that existed originally, the density increased to 3,600 after 24 hours, 5,100 after three days, and to 8,000 after a month. The immediate assimilation of the mineral salts by the bacteria of the vegetable plankton allowed an immediate and considerable increase in every sort of fauna. Plaice, for example, grew in thirteen months as much as ordinarily in two or three years. It is true to say that this was merely an experiment and that we may generalize neither its results nor its bearings. All the same, there seems to be something here which is not chimerical, but a technique for the future. It is still necessary to investigate the commercial aspect of the operation and to assess its importance.[25]

F.A.O. experts estimate that it would be possible easily to double the present world catch of about 25 to 30 million tons, without a risk of exhausting reserves or of endangering catches in the future. This would permit of an important improvement in diets which are deficient in protein. In the world today, the annual consumption of fish hardly reaches ten pounds a head and is less than 1 per cent of the food supply of the human race. In U.S.A. the average consumption of fish is about 10 pounds a head, but in a great part of Latin America fish is practically

[25] A. Guerrin, *Humanité et subsistances*, p. 346.

never eaten. On the side of consumption, therefore, there is much that remains to be done.

The same is true of fresh water fisheries. Insufficient use is made of the resources of rivers and lakes in many countries. A piece of water can give a supply of animal protein far greater than can be had from an equal area of land. This is a precious resource for under-developed countries which are short of food-stuffs of high nutritional value.

ANGOLA

| 1953 | ☐ | 210,000 | (catches in tons) |
| 1956 | ☐ | 400,000 | |

INDIA

1945	☐	505,000
1953	☐	715,000
1958	☐	950,000

PERU

1945	☐	28,000
1958	☐	715,000
1959	☐	1,900,000

NORWAY

1945	☐	810,000
1956	☐	2,100,000
1958	☐	1,430,000

JAPAN

1938	☐	3,350,000
1945	☐	1,900,000
1958	☐	5,200,000

How the catch of fish for some countries has been increasing
(source: F.A.O.)

The "herding" of fish is easily carried on in small ponds. Use can be made either of natural or of artificial bowls. A fisheries plan established in Haiti by an expert of F.A.O.

consisted of the construction of a certain number of breeding tanks, from which were stocked the rivers, streams and lakes which are so numerous in that hilly country. Species were chosen for their rapid growth, among them carp and an African fish, the tilapia, which deserves to be better known for its remarkable qualities.

It multiplies rapidly both in running and in still waters, and whether they are fresh, brackish or salt. It is monogamous and when the eggs have been ejected and fertilized, the mother takes them in her mouth and keeps them there until it is time for them to hatch. The newly hatched fish remain close to their mother for some time and whenever danger threatens they return to the shelter of her mouth.[26]

The tilapia is now used in the fish hatcheries of many countries and with considerable success.

Farmers in Thailand have also stocked their ponds with tilapia and an expert has been working there for four years to develop fisheries in the inland waters. He has organized a network of information services and has instructed a number of officials in the art of fresh water fish farming. Work of the same kind has been undertaken in Ceylon, Guatemala, Honduras, Uganda and Madagascar.

In Asia and America there is a growing association of fish rearing with rice growing. The flooded paddy fields are stocked with young fish, which are either gathered in when the fields are drained or are transferred to fish ponds. Experience has shown that this practice has a double advantage: rice yields are raised by the nitrogen and organic material which is due to the fish having been there, while the fish themselves provide a not inconsiderable quantity of food.[27]

Some countries have rapidly increased their fish catches by the application of relatively simple measures, mainly in matters of technique and marketing, which do not call for heavy investments.

[26] Cf. *Man and Hunger*, p. 61 (F.A.O.).
[27] We can cite an example from U.S.A. A farmer in Arkansas was getting a rice yield of 56 bushels to the acre with the use of manures. He flooded a part of his paddy fields and stocked it with fish. At the end of two years he was getting 250 pounds of fish to the acre, and in the following year his rice yield was up to 100 bushels to the acre. The fish had also rid the paddy fields of weeds.

The first need is to improve the equipment and motive power of the fishing boats. In many tropical countries, fishermen still use primitive equipment and cannot go far out from their coasts. Equipping their boats with engines enables them to go much further and providing them with mechanical means for handling nets enables them at once greatly to increase the size of their catches. In Uganda, for example, nylon nets and outboard motors are being used now in the lake fisheries. Thanks to the financial aid of the Uganda government, there are now 1,200 outboard motors on the lakes. The catch has been doubled and is now more than 48,000 tons a year. There are several other experimental projects in hand, financed by the fund for the development of trade in Africa, which look to the establishment of wholesale and retail fish markets and the provision of storage.

The F.A.O. delegate, Prof. Crutchfield, confirms that the fishing industry in Uganda is in a healthy condition and says that it will grow rapidly once certain bottle-necks in sales and distribution have been removed. Indeed, it is in the preparation of fish—by drying, smoking or other processes—and in the provision of market outlets that many of the under-developed countries find one of their greatest problems. Fishermen on the coast of Chile, for example, often have to throw part of their catch back into the sea because they can find no sale for it, when at the same time people in the interior of the country are having to make do with a diet which is deficient in protein.

This danger of glutting the market is less to be feared in countries which, like Thailand, operate factories for the production of palatable fish meal. The Thailand factory can take 28 tons of fish a day and turn it into 5 tons of meal, using small fish for which it is difficult to find another market. This meal has a protein content which is at least twice as high as that of powdered full cream milk and it is also rich in calcium and vitamin B. Mixed into bread, biscuits, griddle cakes and porridge in the proportion of 6 to 10 per cent, it is quite palatable and does much to balance the people's diet.

VII

FITTING OUT THE CAMPAIGN

NOWADAYS, all who have studied the problem of development in backward countries recognize the necessity of having a general plan to co-ordinate the different sectors of the economy. Otherwise, it will hardly be possible to bring harmoniously into fruitful use the human and material resources which are now so often everywhere unused.

The resources available in different regions vary greatly. Climate, geography, fertility, mineral potentiality and access to capital are all important factors, but there are also questions of population density, and of the political, cultural and social conditions of each country. These are the particular circumstances and potentialities proper to each region which we must make it our business to understand first of all. A plan is of value only to the extent that it is geared to what already exists and allows the fixing of objectives which are within the possibilities of technical and financial resources. Magnificent paper plans have failed before now because, in one respect or other, these factors were under-estimated or ignored.

At Addis Ababa, in 1959, there was a meeting of experts to discuss the general problems raised by economic planning in under-developed countries. What emerged from the meeting was that there are certain indispensable conditions to be satisfied if results of lasting benefit are to be obtained.

The first requirement is that information should be reliable and up-to-date. This demands a certain minimum amount of statistical material on population, production, trade, particularly foreign trade, balance of payments, etc.

Next, there must be a permanent organization competently manned, to work out details and take their repercussions into account and to co-ordinate and supervise development in the different sectors. To this organization would also fall the task of calculating the cost of the development programmes and making provision for the costs of operation and maintenance necessitated by the work in hand.

Alongside this action must go the development of education in all its forms, primary, technical, vocational, and even higher education. The economic future of the under-developed countries is bound up with the quality of the leaders and officials they can train.

In the last place, there was insistence on the necessity for creating a belief in the plan. The mass of the people must be stirred out of its passivity. People must be led to submit themselves to a discipline and agree to a pressure of work and a level of output to which they are ordinarily quite unaccustomed. It is particularly difficult to do this in the rural areas; and everywhere there is need of a better organization to ensure that people accept and work for the plan at the local level.

As for the order of priorities which will have to be established, particularly in what concerns the agricultural and the industrial sectors, there are two sorts of consideration which must be borne in mind.

On the one hand, the investment which is called for by the modernization of agriculture is relatively small. This will be the more true if first attention is given to biological improvements, such as the use of selected seed and improvements in farming methods. This is a matter of prime importance for economics which do not dispose of capital reserves. In any case, an increase in the output of foodstuffs seems to be demanded by humanity where the people are usually under-fed, as well as being the surest means to a progressive raising of the standard of life and purchasing power of the great majority of the population.[1]

On the other hand, there are cases where the pressure of population is very strong and a programme of industrialization must be undertaken to rid the economy of a condition of

---

[1] In this connection, we can quote the judgement of G. Balandier: "To tell the truth, it would seem to be impossible to establish an order of investments which would be generally applicable. Allowance must be made for considerable differences between countries, according to the quality and quantity of exploitable natural resources, the level of development already reached, the quality and training of the labour supply and the intensity of pressure of population. However, it is quite certain that the least contestable, if not the most precise, criterion in the question of choice is that of the general advantage." (*Le Tiers-Monde*, p. 377.)

chronic under-employment which is one of the causes of economic stagnation. Even so, such a programme could with advantage be applied first to the rural industries.[2]

A greater or lesser degree of disguised unemployment is widespread in most of the under-developed countries, where the rural population is still 80 per cent of the whole. This is due as much to periods of seasonal activity as to an excess supply of man-power.

As M. Estrangin emphasized at Angers,

> seasonal variations in the demand for labour in agriculture present a problem in every part of the world, but particularly in tropical and sub-tropical countries and in the over-populated countries of the far east. Before the coming of communism, the Chinese worked 125 days a year; the Malagasy, sometimes 100, but sometimes only 40; the African also 100, at the best 150, sometimes less than 60.[3]

In the Philippines, the growers of rice, of coconuts and of tobacco spend an average of four months in agricultural work and the maize growers spend six months. An investigation based on samples, made by the Central Bank of Ceylon, gives reason to believe that out of a working population of about 3,200,000, some 386,000, or 12 per cent of the total, work less than 20 hours a week. A similar enquiry in India showed that adult agricultural workers are employed an average of 218 days a year; but this figure differs considerably between different regions, ranging from 289 days in the north of the country to only 181 in the south. It is the judgement of F.A.O. that this is a phenomenon which is widespread in Asia, where rural workers are idle for more than one-third of the time.

It is well known that under-employment is chronic also in the Near East and in Egypt particularly. There a peasant family on average farms only 1·6 acres, where it could easily manage an area five times as great, using the same equipment. Under-

---

[2] At an international conference on "The Politics of Development" which was held in Israel in the summer of 1960, emphasis was laid on the place which agriculture should have in these programmes. "The major part," observed P. Rondot, "will not be played by academic people, but by better instructed farmers and skilled workers who have been released from the power of the great land-owners and the money-lenders."

[3] Semaine Sociale of Angers, 1959: *La montée des Peuples dans la Communauté humaine.*

employment is widespread also in Lebanon, although in a less acute form than in Egypt. In Syria, Iraq and Iran there are not enough agricultural workers to cultivate all the land that can be cultivated, but even so under-employment is not less present there, because of the irrational way in which the land is distributed and the inefficient way in which the work is organized.

The situation is not much better in several of the Latin American countries, where the small cultivator often has much too small a piece of land on which to work. On the high plateaux in Bolivia, an Indian family has at its disposal on the average only 0·8 of an acre. An enquiry in the Pichincha region in Ecuador showed that out of 941 farms investigated, 709 had an area varying between $\frac{1}{2}$ and 2 acres. In consequence of increasing soil exhaustion, the Indians of Peru suffer from a state of chronic under-employment which is becoming acute.

The same problem exists in Central America and in the West Indies. In Guatemala, where more than half the farms are of less than $3\frac{1}{2}$ acres, agricultural labour is under-employed. The same is true of Jamaica and Puerto Rico, where under-employment of rural workers often reaches 40 per cent.

Where under-employment of this nature persists it is difficult to hope for a raising of the standard of living and an improvement in the people's diet. Being idle for so much of their time, these peasants cannot buy enough to provide for their essential needs. More often than not there is no alternative employment within their reach and so they find themselves condemned to a life of poverty.

According to M. Gabriel Ardant,[4] there are in the under-developed countries at least 200,000,000 men who are without work for 100 days a year. This comes to 20,000,000,000 days lost each year. This unused labour power is a source of wealth which can be a means to the development of these so very backward countries.

What has been happening in China, where the weight of change has been carried largely by the country people, gives us a glimpse of what can be done by the systematic application of human labour, whether to a multitude of small measures of improvement or the building of large dams by simple techniques.

[4] G. Ardant, *Le Monde en friche* (1959).

To construct the dam in the Ming valley, 400,000 "volunteers" worked 160 days, carrying on their shoulders in the traditional coolie's basket a total of some 2,250,000 cubic yards of soil, stone and sand. Similarly, to cut a canal in the depth of winter, with the temperature several degrees below freezing point, a multitude of peasants moved a veritable mountain of earth, each having no equipment other than a little Chinese basket suspended on a bamboo pole.[5]

As a result of his journey to Morocco in 1957, M. Ardant was able to confirm on the spot the value of projects undertaken by the body of local people, examples being clearing fields of stones, sinking wells, clearing streams, planting trees, cutting drainage ditches, etc. He believes that it is possible to make use of unemployed labour on the spot to carry through, at village or district level, many small projects which are adapted to the local needs. In his opinion, it would be a mistake to depend entirely on help from outside to solve the problems of the under-developed countries: the technical and financial aid which the more advanced countries can give would be meaningless if it were not accompanied by effort on the part of the communities concerned to help themselves.

Quite simple little jobs which can be done by the people for themselves, with or without the help of technicians, can do much to improve the productivity of a district.

Several projects of this kind have been put in hand in Morocco, notably in the provinces of Marrakesh and Agadir and in the Taffilal. The job at Sidi Rahal was removing stones from 15,000 acres which were carpeted with them. The whole of a Berber tribe, numbering some 8,000 persons in 2,000 households, worked under the direction of their chiefs and the team-leaders, care having been taken to explain to them beforehand the value of the undertaking. The local authorities gave an example by gathering up stones with the rest and the people submitted willingly to this discipline of collective work. On average, each family received 7,500 francs, half in cash and the remainder in wheat, the total outlay coming to 15,000,000 francs. It was reckoned that the result was an increase in yield from the land of four quintals an acre; that is to say, 60,000 quintals

---

[5] Reports from J. Jacquet-Francillon in *Le Figaro*.

more of wheat or barley which, at an average price of 2,500 francs, is worth 150,000,000 francs. This is the sort of return to be expected from a really productive investment.[6]

In the province of Agadir, the project was one of tree planting and, at Lembad, 750 acres were broken up and planted with almond trees. In the opinion of M. René Dumont, who has studied Moroccan rural problems in detail, priority ought to be given to works which will lead to an increase in useful employment and in production, pride of place being given to small-scale water undertakings, such as the tapping of local water resources, cementing water channels or pumping from wells.

Modernization is not to be sought after at any cost. In the Chaouia, to the south of Settat, not far from Oumer R'bia, there is water not far down, but a well has so slight a flow that the water must as yet be raised by animals who, of course, have to have their handlers. A mechanical pump would be kept unemployed for long periods while the well was filling again.[7]

At a later stage, works should be undertaken which would lift from the people the burden of unproductive tasks: piped water and afforestation would "relieve the people of the interminable carting of water and of wood which goes on in too many Mediterannean villages". Much can be done also by the "erection of dykes against erosion, running parallel to contour lines and across the angle of the slope. These walls could be planted with trees—olives, figs, almonds, nuts, which give shade and fruit and do well in Moroccan soil."

These works, however, require workers with sufficient technical training for their direction. "To trace the line of a water channel or a contour dyke calls for knowledge of how to use a dumpy level. And the mixing of concrete calls for some precision." These over-lookers and foremen should be chosen from the villages. They can be trained very rapidly and then returned to their homes to put their knowledge at the service of the locality.

[6] G. Ardant, loc. cit.

[7] René Dumont, "Problèmes agricoles du Maroc indépendant", in *Économie rurale*, Jan. 1958.

Since 1958, Tunisia has been proceeding along the same lines, carrying out work on the restoration of the soil, making plantations, digging wells and irrigation channels. The most urgent thing, then, is not always to be aiming at costly investments. There are some improvements which can be carried out by local communities themselves and which will improve conditions of production appreciably. Often, however, the primary problem is to know how to arouse the local people from their state of passivity.

At the time of our passing through the district of Bolpur in West Bengal, there had not been spent there one rupee of the 200,000 rupees which had been put at the disposal of the district solely for providing small water works. And this was despite the fact that there were great gains to be had from such works in this district, where only 4 per cent of the cultivated land was devoted to crops other than rice and an even smaller proportion was double cropped.[8]

It is often necessary to undertake schemes which cover a wide area and which can be of fundamental importance to the development of an entire district. This is particularly the case as regards the water resources of a country or region.

It rarely happens that the water resources of under-developed countries are exploited as they could be. Countries which are watered by large rivers submit by turns to droughts and floods and for thousands of years nobody has attempted to alter this sequence of events. We have only to recall, for example, that in the province of Uttar Pradesh, in India, in 1948, the Ganges overflowed its banks and put 3,500,000 acres of cultivated ground under water, washed away 4,000 villages and made 4,000,000 people homeless. In the same year, the Indus flooded 460,000 acres of good land and damaged or destroyed 3,500 villages in West Pakistan. There is no need to comment on these figures: in themselves, they are sufficient evidence of the importance of remedial measures.

In Burma and Viet-Nam and in other countries, rivers which for part of their courses are confined in narrow gorges will

[8] René Dumont, "Le Mouvement du 'développement communautaire en Inde' ", in *Économie rurale*, July–Sept. 1959.

sometimes spread extensively when they emerge into the plain and transform vast tracts of fertile land into lakes.

Since the last war, conferences of experts have considered means which could be used to control the floods of Asia. Protective measures have been studied by interested countries, such as India, Pakistan, Ceylon, Burma, Cambodia and Viet-Nam, and help has been given to them by international technical experts. Often, measures designed primarily for flood control will be bound up with a far-reaching programme of economic development, the principal components of which will be the construction of large hydro-electric undertakings and schemes for industrialization of the region.

The harnessing of great rivers for purely agricultural purposes is a long term project, in any case, calling for the building of expensive dams and pumping stations and the cutting of irrigation networks and drainage systems over vast areas to serve large numbers of farmers. Often, help must be obtained from foreign engineers and construction companies. All large scale plans for water management must rest on a general plan which provides for the optimum use both of land and water over a wide area.

Sometimes, an irrigation system can be supplied with water from reservoirs established in natural depressions and modern developments in aerial survey and photography have made it much easier to discover such places. Their utilization will prevent flooding, as well as provide water for irrigation. Two examples of this method are to be found in Iraq. A reservoir at Habbaniya will impound 3,430,000, million cubic yards of water from the Euphrates; and another at Oued Tharthar will impound 100,000 million cubic yards from the Tigris. These reservoirs are filled by means of canals which lead the river water into the depressions. A dam on the Euphrates will help to fill the reservoirs at Habbaniya at times when the river is not in spate.

The River Gash, which rises in Eritrea and flows through the Sudan, has long periods of flood, lasting about 80 days. Its waters have been put to use through a simple system of diversion. A network of canals has been built to carry the water away from the river itself to irrigate an area of nearly 50,000 acres, two-thirds of which carry crops of high quality cotton. A similar experimental scheme has been tried out around

Kushtia, on the right bank of the Ganges in Eastern Pakistan. There, the waters of the Ganges and the Brahmaputra are used to irrigate an area of 232,000 acres. Experts working under the Colombo Plan have helped in these projects and a French company carried out the engineering.

An agreement between India and Pakistan has made possible the completion of a vast irrigation project in the Indus basin. The International Bank for Reconstruction and Development (I.B.R.D.) is helping in the financing of the scheme, one of the largest of this nature which has been attempted up to now. The annual flow of the Indus and the five tributaries which flow into it from the left is more than three times that of the Nile and ten times that of the Colorado River in U.S.A. The flow of water each year would be enough to flood a plain equal to the area of the whole of France to a depth of one foot. The cost of the project is estimated at 1,070,000,000 dollars, 870,000,000 for the Pakistan side and 200,000,000 for the Indian side. On the Pakistan side there will be eight canals totalling more than 400 miles in length and irrigating 5,000,000 acres of land; at least two reservoirs, one on the Jhelum at Mangla, and another on the Indus at Tarbela; and the construction of a generating station at Mangla of 300,000 kw. installed capacity. On the Indian side, there will be a dam across the River Beas which will provide for the irrigation of Rajasthan and the generation of 200,000 kw.

Ten years ago Ceylon began work on the task of bringing into use the arid zone of the Gal Oya valley. This enterprise is to be compared with the work of the Tennessee Valley Authority in U.S.A. or of the Niger Administration in the former French Sudan. The Gal Oya Development Board, which is the organizing authority, has in view an interconnected system of major projects. What is intended is the reconstruction of a main hydro-electric station, the regeneration of the valley lands and their colonization. Ten dams have been built to hold back the flood waters and more than forty villages fitted out, complete with their co-operatives and their schools. Others are to follow. In this region, formerly quite empty, the plan is to settle 200,000 people. The colonists will not have to depend upon the traditional hand tools and animal power; they are being supplied with tractors and other mechanical equipment, and central workshops have been established for their maintenance and repair. The scheme could not have been undertaken but for the help given under the Colombo Plan, by the I.B.R.D. and by the technical experts lent by F.A.O.

Undertakings of this size, which are necessarily very costly and dependent upon outside help, must be few. Their importance is rather as experimental projects which show what can follow from the recovery of a region which had formerly been thought of as useless.

A problem which calls for solution in most of the countries of the Near and Middle East is that of afforestation. This is bound up with the problems of the maintenance of soil fertility and management of nomadic pastures. Syria, Jordan and Iraq were all in former times covered with forests; and as the forests have disappeared, so have the deserts grown and erosion claimed new lands. In these parts, a place has to be found in programmes of reconstruction for reafforestation. The success of this work depends to a large extent on the degree to which grazing can be controlled, particularly of the goats; and to which water can be prevented from washing soil away down the hill slopes. Measures are already being taken along these lines. In Iraq there are two distinct climatic zones to be dealt with and each calls for special treatment. One measure to which particular attention is being given is that of planting quick growing species of trees, such as poplars and eucalyptus, both to provide firewood and to establish wind-breaks between the irrigated areas and the arid lands. In the wet areas the important thing is to establish a system of good forest management.

The culture of olives is being encouraged again in Libya, and in Cyrenaica the vineyards are beginning to flourish again. Olive growing in Libya fell into neglect after the departure of the Italian farmers and the Libyan government has now in hand a twenty year plan to restore olive growing to its former importance. An olive nursery provides 600,000 young trees to the Libyan cultivators and demonstrations are organized, particularly to show the farmers how to use elaborate spraying equipment in their plantations. In Cyrenaica, work is going on to replant the ancient vineyards in the districts of Messa, Beida and Gubba, which used to supply Europe with fine wine and table grapes, as well as to plant new vine growing areas.

It has been shown in a number of cases that it is usually better not to attempt to leap into the industrial age in under-developed countries where the greater part of the population is still engaged in agriculture and is very backward. It is not always wise to want to go straight from the hoe and the wooden plough to the complications of electro-chemical techniques and machine tools.

Too fast a pace of industrialization tends to widen the gap between the rural and the urban populations and this brings grave social and economic disturbances in its train. In several parts of tropical Africa, too quick a growth of large urban and industrial centres has brought into existence an unsettled working class, of little worth, ill trained and unstable. Around the large centres there is a rash of shanty-towns, places which are dangerous to both health and morals; while in the countryside, which has been emptied of its young people, those who are left cannot raise enough food even for subsistence.

We have described elsewhere[9] the consequences which too fast a pace of change have for established order. What seems to be required is a transitional stage, in which small rural industries would be developed and the artisan class encouraged to modernize itself. These small industries, based on the processing of agricultural produce, stimulate production and raise purchasing power in the country districts and absorb the under-employed farm population.

In most cases, it is desirable for these small industries to make use of local raw materials; otherwise, it may be found necessary very often to undertake really heavy investments. Examples would be saw-mills, tanneries, oil distilleries, ginning mills, small cloth mills, carpentry, pottery and other artisanal undertakings. Later, the prosperity of these modernized rural industries would form a basis from which an advance could be made to a greater degree of industrialization.

F.A.O. technical advisers have already done much in several countries to further the growth of such industries, notably for the skins and hide industries of India. It was a matter of urgency to get a better return from the very large cattle population there, for the traditional methods were enormously wasteful, producing goods of very poor quality which were difficult

[9] Vide *Pays sous-developpées et coopération technique*, pp. 117–123.

to sell. The establishment of centres where better methods could be demonstrated and taught has led to a rapid increase in the number of competent people. In consequence, the value of the industry's products has risen some 30 to 40 per cent. In the state of Uttar Pradesh, where the first experiments were made, these centres were organized on a co-operative basis within the framework of the government's plan. The effect on the leather trade there has been considerable. In some villages there has been a rapid growth in the artisanal trade of shoe making, output having quickly reached 15,000 pairs a day.

In Burma and Afghanistan, advisers are helping to develop the culture of silk worms and the associated artisanal industries. The programme of development includes the introduction of improved varieties of mulberry trees, extensive replanting and the importation of selected strains of silk worms from Japan. In Burma, the rearing of silk worms has been undertaken by a number of co-operatives and workshops have been built in the rural areas to wind the threads. Formerly, in Afghanistan, the rearing of silk worms was carried on only around Kabul and Baghlan, but now it has spread to other rural areas and several thousands of families are engaged in it. The silk which is being produced locally competes successfully with imported materials, which are often of an inferior quality.

Crude rubber production in Thailand is thriving now that better bearing trees have been introduced. Formerly, rubber was produced by small planters with fewer than 200 acres at their disposal, living a poor and precarious existence at the mercy of world fluctuations in the price of raw rubber. An F.A.O. adviser has been able to get better varieties of trees planted and better methods of treating the raw materials introduced into reorganized factories. The small producers are now able to sell their product at the highest going price.

Chad, in the former French Equatorial Africa, is a poor enough country, but there is a well developed cattle rearing industry in the central districts with some 4,000,000 head of cattle and as many of sheep. An abattoir has been established at Farcha to serve the export trade. Designed on a modern basis, it will process 8,000 tons of meat a year, while allied industries have been established to deal with the hides and other by-products. The meat is carried by air to the other great

African centres of population, such as Brazzaville, Duala, Yaunde and Leopoldville.

Examples such as these could be multiplied. All show how important it is to develop, in rural areas, local industries which will be complementary to farming activities.

The F.A.O. has lately put before interested governments proposals for the better management of progress towards industrialization of the countryside. The emphasis would be on providing means and encouragement to rural dwellers to learn how to make better use of the natural resources which are now so very often not used: stone, wood, wool, skins, clay, reeds, fibres, etc. There could be increased production of agricultural implements and vehicles, as well as of household goods, each group of farms or villages specializing on articles based on the technical possibilities open to it and the materials which were at its disposal. This would be the first step towards real technical competence and greater productivity for the country peoples and also greater self-confidence. The campaign would last until rural industries had been established capable of producing goods which were able to stand up to competition in commercial markets.

In some countries, particularly in the rural areas, there have been interesting experiments in community development. The method has been used much in India and Pakistan to promote modernization in the countryside. Experiments are also being tried in Africa, under a somewhat different form, while the role the collectives have played in Israel is well known.

The programme of organizing rural communities began in India in 1952 and a little later in Pakistan, the projects in the two countries being very similar. The basis on which the plan rests is essentially the small team of leaders which has a many-sided role, being charged with the tasks of animating and managing activities in every field, whether agricultural, social or cultural.

The basic unit adopted by the administrators of the Agricultural and Development Programme in Pakistan is a sector which includes about 150 villages with a population of from 130,000 to 160,000 people. The aim is not simply to increase agricultural outputs, but also to improve the living conditions of the people, their education, hygiene, housing, local industries, and social and recreational activities.[10]

The method is to make people learn by *doing*. It is sought to arouse their interest in a project which would produce a small but urgently necessary improvement and to ask for their active co-operation in completing the project.

Between 1954 and 1959 the number of sectors established was 134. In West Pakistan each sector has 30 advisers attached to it, while in East Pakistan each has only 20 advisers: that is to say, in West Pakistan there is one adviser for every five villages, while in East Pakistan there is only one for every six or seven villages. Usually, the advisers are natives of the areas in which they work and have completed a secondary or university education. In addition, they have all followed a course of training lasting a year in one of the twelve institutes established for this purpose.

Results obtained during the first five years of the programme's working seem to justify its methods. The first task of the advisers was to convince the farmers of the benefits they would derive from using selected seed and increasing the cultivation of fruit trees and vegetables. Better seed was in fact used by 88,600 farmers on more than 160,000 acres, 85,000 acres were planted to fruit trees and vegetable cultivation grew even more rapidly. At the same time, they were persuaded to make use of insecticides, dig compost pits and apply artificial manures. In addition to all this, 180,000 acres were irrigated by means of more than 750 miles of newly dug channels; the opening of veterinary centres made possible the inoculation against disease of 1,500,000 head of cattle, and on the level of professional organization, more than 1,500 co-operatives were established and those which already existed were improved.

Finally, there was a particularly impressive achievement in school building. Up to September 1958, 1,028 schools were built or reconstructed. This provided an average of one school for every 15 villages; and today, there is one school for every 10 villages.

The operation is financed partly by the sector administrations, partly by the groups which benefit from its activities. Funds

[10] Vide U.N.E.S.C.O, *International Review of the Social Sciences*, 60, no. 3. Part of our documentation is taken from this work.

amounting to about 40,000 dollars a year are put at the disposal
of each sector to be allocated to approved development projects.
The people themselves provide whatever materials and labour
may be necessary.

The Indian community extension plan, begun in 1952, had
reached 85,000 villages by 1954 and today affects 250,000. Here
also some important results have been achieved, although
success has been somewhat patchy. As a result of his investigations in India, René Dumont has pointed to certain deficiencies
in the equipment of the team organizers, all of whom doubtless
have their diplomas, but some of whom lack some indispensable
experience.

When the student leaves his agricultural college, he should
be seconded to a village for a year's obligatory service. This
reform would provide young and dynamic leaders for the
developing community. At the same time, the future agro-
nomist would receive a practical apprenticeship which would
make him much more valuable in later years, whether in the
laboratory, as a field adviser or as an official.

It must have become very quickly apparent that the success
of the community development scheme rested on the active
participation of the women, and for this reason a special department was set up in the organization to put in hand a programme
of women's activity. This programme looked to maternal and
child care; hygiene; agricultural work and connected occupations, such as managing a kitchen garden, looking after cattle
and chickens, etc.; cottage industries, like spinning, weaving,
basket-making; the rearing of children and domestic economy;
and recreational and cultural activities.

A major difficulty arose out of the scarcity of women leaders.
To remedy this defect, short courses were organized to train
likely country women to assist the leaders who were anyway too
few in number. This system, begun in Uttar Pradesh and
Rajasthan, has now become general and almost everywhere one
finds local volunteers who are paid a small stipend for the
work they do.

In a country like India, where the basis of agriculture is the
family farm, the women are closely associated with the work of
the fields. They do not undertake the heavy work, but they do

supply a large part of the labour for other tasks, such as sowing, planting out, weeding and even the building of terraces. People discuss the example of one village, where it was the women who persuaded their husbands to use fertilizers and selected seed. The adviser had failed in his task of persuasion and had turned the problem over to his woman assistant. It was the custom for the village women to plant vegetable seeds in pots in the hall where they met to do their sewing. The woman assistant planted a grain of wheat of the local variety in one pot and a grain of selected seed in another, repeating the operation in two other pots, each of which contained some fertilizer. To each pot she gave a name, so that they acquired a sort of personality. The women watched the growth of the plants as though it were a race and, when the corn was grown, called in the senior farmers, good judges in these matters, to declare which grain of seed had bred the winner. But there was no need for a judgement; the superiority of the selected seed grown in the fertilized pot was obvious. Now, the whole village will use none but selected seed and swears by the use of fertilizer.

In another field of activity, the Khadi Commission, charged with the task of encouraging village spinning and winding, has persuaded the women to adopt the use of an improved wheel for cotton spinning. This enables the cottage worker to do all the operations from carding to skeining and have an output for an eight hour working day of six skeins of thread, almost twice as much as was being produced formerly. The second five-year plan looks to the delivery of some 2,500,000 of these pieces of equipment.[11]

The part which women are playing in the economic development of the countryside has the additional consequence of doing much to change their way of life. Women are escaping more and more from close seclusion in the home and are learning trades

[11] Almost throughout India, the women are taking an increasingly active part in the different sectors of the economy. More than 80 per cent of working women are employed in agriculture and related occupations. The growing industrialization of the country has opened up to women possibilities of employment in the new industries which are replacing the old artisanal occupations. A sample taken recently in the industries which are in process of transformation showed that women form 81 per cent of the labour force in ground-nut shelling, 42 per cent in the tobacco industry, 35 per cent in the match industry, 31 per cent in cotton ginning, 25 per cent in the processing of rice, fruits and vegetables, and 21 per cent in lime and brickmaking plants. (*International Labour Review*, "Women's Employment in India", April, 1959.)

outside the range of the hereditary family occupations. What is more, they are now to be seen taking part in village meetings with people from different castes, something which is altogether new.

Two examples will illustrate this changing state of affairs. There has been completed lately in Rajasthan a large dam which has been built by the voluntary labour of 8,000 men and 3,000 women from the neighbouring villages. Elsewhere, out of 22 women in a camp where they were doing their course of training as social assistants, one was an untouchable, a *harijan*. Despite this, she was allowed to take her place in a team of three charged with the duty of cooking the meals, something which would formerly have been quite inconceivable.[12]

All this is an indication of the profound change which is slowly taking place in the social customs of India, a transformation which is tending to the liberation of souls from the crushing weight of traditions which, as we have seen, form a grave handicap to progress, in the best sense of that word. But, just as in those parts of Africa which are influenced by Mohammedanism or animism, the emancipation of woman is yet to come.

For some years now, Ghana has been doing much the same as India and Pakistan to encourage community development, but with what appears to be a slighter and more flexible administrative framework.[13]

The mainspring of the whole movement is the Mass Education Assistant. He is the person who is responsible for the development of a village or group of villages and the active participation and initiative of the people in them. His work is primarily psychological in nature. He lives in the village, organizes discussion meetings and suggests the things which could be improved. If a project calls for some special skill, he applies to the Community Development Officers, who are the specialists attached to the movement. These can call upon the appropriate technical services, relying on the field engineers, for example, or the agricultural service, if what is in question is the construction of an irrigation network or some drainage works.

[12] Vide "The place of women in the community development programme in India", by Mrs Parimal Das: *International Labour Review*, July 1959.

[13] G. Dulphy, "Au Ghana, expériences multiformes et concluantes" in *Développement et civilisation de l'IRFED*, June 1960.

Mass education assistants are selected from young men of 23 years of age who have completed their primary education. They do a training course of nine months, including six months of practical experience in a rural formation centre, before being allowed to work in a village.

Ghanaian community development was quickly brought to take a particular interest in the formation of young people. These are grouped into units called Builders' Brigades, a name which is indicative of their spirit and purpose. Unemployed young men or those who have "volunteered" are put into these groups and subjected to a military type of discipline. They receive a civic and social education and are taught a trade and afterwards the government helps them to establish themselves in the country districts.

The same sort of work is going on in Morocco, Togoland and Senegal, although with perhaps less official guidance, the impulsion coming from I.R.A.M. and I.R.F.E.D., who want to be able to designate leaders of village groups from among the villagers themselves and train them by short intensive courses in their tasks.

The first Moroccan experiment in the province of Marrakesh brought such good results that the Sherifian government is asking for its extension to the whole country. The problem now is how to coordinate this activity with the economic plan and, in particular, how to integrate with it the various technical services and farm credit institutions, which exist to encourage and support the basic tasks being undertaken by the rural communities.

The Togoland experiment is being carried on in the central mountains, where the people are already progressive and will lend themselves readily to action of this sort. Senegal, which is already quite considerably developed, offers favourable ground and the scheme has quickly seized the imaginations of the young people. The B.D.P.A. (Office for the Development of Agricultural Production Overseas) is doing similar work in African negro states, running short courses of instruction for rural counsellors and trying to provide for the African villages leaders who are good all-rounders.[14]

The well-known Israeli farm collectives take two forms, the *kibbutzim*, which are communal villages, and the *moshavim*,

[14] Vide *Pays sous-développés et coopération technique*, pp. 181 ff.

which are co-operatives of small peasant farmers. These experiments have a very different social context. The people are much more advanced and the task of arousing their initiative has to be approached in a different way. In addition, both types employ the most modern agricultural techniques: tractors, combine harvesters, fertilizers, controlled cattle feeding, artificial insemination, electric incubators, etc. Rarely have works of land improvement been carried so far, particular attention being paid to irrigation systems which make it possible to reap very good crops from otherwise arid soil.

The *kibbutz* is somewhat totalitarian in idea, being based on common use of land, capital and labour and even communal housing and living conditions. It has been made possible only by the idealism which pushes a people to the mastery of its own land, a spirit which characterized the early days of the new state. It is no longer the expanding force that it was, its place having been taken by the village co-operative, the *moshav*, an organizational type which is less extreme and safeguards the liberties and private initiative of everyone.[15]

It must be emphasized, however, that with both types of settlement the driving force is the free decisions of the people who are immediately concerned and whose responsibility it is to conduct their own affairs. The system is not prescribed by the government, nor are the people constrained to it, as is the case in new countries which are under communist rule.

Besides, it does not seem that the totalitarian regimes have found in their agrarian policies the sort of answer which will improve matters and satisfy real needs. A discontent which holds back progress is frequent even among the Chinese production teams, who are committed to a heavy burden of labour from which the peasant masses draw very little profit. It is not at all rare to hear people grumble that "five pounds of sweet potatoes which are yours and which you can eat are worth more than a half-million pounds of rice that you may only look at". As M. Edouard Bonnefous has observed, in these last few years the democratic republics have seen "agrarian unrest bubble over and even sometimes shake the government, without any durable solution being found which would put an end to

---

[15] L. Barjon, "Quinze jours au kibboutz" in *Études*, Dec. 1960.

the troubles".[16] Recent disillusionments with agricultural policies in both Russia and China which have been mentioned in the press do nothing to invalidate this judgement.

Supported by J.A.C. and M.I.J.A.R.C. (Jeunesse Agricole Catholique and Mouvement International de la Jeunesse Agricole et Rurale Catholique), the Catholic rural organizations have been at work since 1956 on the task of training young negro countrymen in the states which were formerly French West Africa and French Equatorial Africa. Their campaign is now beginning to bring results.

More than twenty leaders of the French J.A.C. and J.A.C.F., as well as some from other countries, have spent from one to three years in Africa, going from village to village to get groups organized. Classes have been held on the spot to train indigenous leaders to take their place as the "animators" of these groups.

After six years of this work there are now in the former French West Africa more than 2,000 groups of boys and girls, the organization being particularly well advanced in Senegal, Upper Volta and the Ivory Coast; while in the former French Equatorial Africa, where work began later, there are about 250 groups.

Some of the African leaders are sent to France for a stay of from two months to a year, when they are welcomed into the homes of French peasant families.[17]

What these young people are doing overseas is well worth while, being adapted to local needs as much on the level of leisure activities as on that of working life, housing and the changing patterns of the traditional way of life. One example of this comes from the Lobi country, where the action of the local J.A.C. has reduced the bride price—a grave handicap in the way of young people wishing to marry—from ten to two head of cattle.

An example of action on housing comes from Gilongou, in Upper Volta. On the occasion of the wedding of a J.A.C. member, the young people, helped with some technical advice, set to work to make bricks and to build a house. The team of

---

[16] E. Bonnefous, op. cit., p. 350.

[17] Other types of training allow young French peasants to go abroad, while about 50 trainees from various countries of Africa and South America are looked after each year by the J.A.C.

young men went on to build a score of three- and four-roomed houses, types which were a great improvement on the old dark and dirty huts. The young women gave a helping hand by carrying water for the making of mortar. The fame of the Gilongou team spread and they were called upon to do the same in other villages. To provide work in this way to young men in their own places is the best means of combatting the exodus from the country which is the curse of these parts.

The groups give great importance to leisure activities, for the Africans are very fond of entertainments. Songs, theatrical performances and dancing mimes are always greatly appreciated and certain of success everywhere. In the lower Ivory Coast, to take but one example, there are about forty centres for recreational activity.

J.A.C. members have done a great deal to improve the people's working lives, attending to the cultivation of cottage gardens, planting of fruit trees, harnessing of donkeys and cattle, improvements to irrigation systems, founding co-operative purchasing agencies, etc. Cattle are virtually unknown in most African villages. The consequence is that not only does the soil suffer from lack of manuring, but also use cannot be made of the plough. Urged on by the young people, several places have begun to use animals for haulage work and at Koudougou, for example, they have even begun to make light carts of a type suited to the district. In the district of Imansgho, in Upper Volta, donkeys used to run half wild, being used only for pack transport; now they are being harnessed to work in the fields and a J.A.C. delegate from Luxembourg has set up a small workshop to make donkey collars for them. At first the old men resisted the change, but slowly the advantages of using the plough instead of the mattock became appreciated and it was soon necessary to enlarge the workshop and engage workmen to increase its output. The people have been brought to sow their seed in drills, not broadcast as formerly, and to control the breeding of their sheep and goats scientifically. The J.A.C. members have also taught them how to make use of bottom lands and neglected bits of bush for growing vegetables and planting orchards, which are all too rare in that part of the world.

The young countrywomen of Africa have just as much need of help to show them how to improve their conditions, as the following extract from a letter of a member of the J.A.C.F. shows:

> On my journeys through Senegal and Upper Volta, I have seen the good work which is being done by many groups which were established only last year. The young women have banded themselves together to fight against the custom of trial marriage: they cultivate plantations in common so as to have a little money from the sale of what they grow: in many villages, they meet together to learn to read and write, to sew and iron and manage a house. The great difficulty is the lack of competent women to help them. I have known young women who have had to depend upon the nun at the dispensary 25 miles away from their village for some elementary instruction on hygiene.[18]

The impressive congress which M.I.J.A.R.C. held at Lourdes in May 1960, to which 25,000 young country people came from all parts of the world, was a visible manifestation of this work among them. One of the most moving episodes of an assembly of peoples such as has never before been seen was the offering of the fruits and products of their native lands by delegates of the 60 countries represented there. Brazil sent coffee, and Chile a casket; from Senegal came ground-nuts and from Dahomey, fruits; Upper Volta and Togo sent rice and beans; from Gabon came bananas and from Chad, pineapples and cotton; scarves came from Madagascar and Viet-Nam sent beautifully finished works of art.

---

[18] Letter from Mlle. Marie-Thérèse S. . . ., dated 13 May 1959. Some weeks after that date, this brave young woman was struck down by poliomyelitis while travelling through the Senegalese bush and taken to hospital at Dakar, where she was put into an iron lung. She is now in hospital near Paris, on the long road back to recovery.

VIII

THE ROLE OF EDUCATION

IMPROVEMENT in the standards of feeding in backward countries is not entirely a matter of economics or of technical arrangements. There are some countries which produce enough to provide for their needs and yet show clear evidence of a nutritional deficiency which is sometimes grave. The cause of this sort of situation is to be found in harmful customs.

It is necessary, therefore, to enter upon an educational campaign at the same time as action is being taken to improve production. There is added reason for this in areas where the people are illiterate and where custom and tradition are often bound up with religious beliefs and have to some extent the sacredness of a divine law.

In many countries, the customary diet is ordained by traditions which are very much more than mere customs. It is not enough to find out what it is that the people eat: it will also be useful to know what special virtue is supposed to lie in each article of food. In some Far Eastern countries, for example, rice, which is the basic food of the people, is regarded almost with veneration, the people believing that without it they cannot have either health or strength. This explains why rice is introduced into the diet of children at a very early age, even at the risk of causing digestive troubles. In other parts of the world it is maize, served as a porridge or as pancakes, or some other cereal to which is assigned this role.

It is by no means rare to meet with beliefs that some foodstuffs guard against sickness and some against misfortune, possessing particular strengthening virtues, while others cause epilepsy or impotence. Beliefs such as these are frequently associated with pregnancy and childbirth; consequently, they exert a strong influence on the feeding of both mother and child.

Sometimes it is milk and eggs which are forbidden them, sometimes fish.

Some small tribes have dietary rules which reveal an obsession with questions of "purity". It appears to the primitive mind that contact with certain things which have incompatible "souls" can set in train powerful magic causing sterility or disease. Thus, the Bahimas of South Africa never have vegetables and milk at the same meal. The Suks and other tribes never eat millet and dairy produce together. Above all, care must be taken not to consume meat and milk at the same time. Among the Naudis, it is necessary to refrain from using milk products for several weeks after any meat has been eaten.[1] Similar commands are to be found, of course, in Deuteronomy.

As Dr Jelliffe has remarked:

> The peoples who inhabit the greater part of South-east Asia did not at one time think of animal milk as a foodstuff fit for human consumption, even for the youngest babies. There is reason to believe that they are now ready to use tinned or powdered milk because these do not remind them of a cow.

It is necessary then, when any attempt is being made to improve a people's eating habits, to take into account the ideas and beliefs on which those habits are founded. This is the verdict of the joint committee of F.A.O. and W.H.O.

> New eating habits will be accepted only to the extent that they become integrated into the existing system of beliefs and ideas. The ethnologist can help the nutritionist, the sanitation expert, the agricultural specialist and the social service administrator to discover just where they stand when they come up against this problem.[2]

A custom of diet is often a point of a creed: to change one, it is necessary often also to change the other. In other cases it is necessary only to remove misunderstandings, as is shown in this report of Dr Tremollières:

[1] Dr Claudian, "Le jeûne dans les civilizations primitives et dans les religions du passé" in *Redécouverte du jeûne*, 1959.

[2] F.A.O.-W.H.O. Joint Committee, *Report of the fourth session*, 1955.

In a poor Moroccan village I saw stocks of powdered milk which had been allowed to become so tainted as to be unfit even to be fed to the cattle, because nobody there thought of it as a foodstuff. I saw the same thing happen with canned milk in Greece, after the famine of 1943.

It is said that in Morocco the people refused to eat the cream cheese which is sold under the trade mark of *La Vache qui rit*, a rumour having spread that they were expected to feed their children on stuff which in France was fed to the cows.

It would seem that the more simple and primitive the life which people lead, the more likely are they to be distrustful of any dietary innovation. It is only by means of a methodical process of education that they can slowly be brought to accept change.

Education in dietary matters in under-developed countries must satisfy certain conditions if it is to lead to lasting results. It would be a mistake to go bald-headed at a people with strong traditions and try to get them to change their feeding habits. Failure would be certain.

Whoever is charged with the task of bringing people to make a change must be thoroughly well documented on the population he is being called upon to deal with. Not only must he know what home grown foods are commonly eaten and how they are prepared for table, but also he must be familiar with the types of fuel, of fireplace and of kitchen utensils used. It will often be necessary for him to frequent the market places and keep himself informed on seasonal changes in the availability of foodstuffs and in their prices. Particular attention will have to be given to local methods of feeding infants, note being taken of the fact that these can vary from district to district. In the same way, notice must be taken of the ways in which the period of breast-feeding and methods of weaning can differ from one place to another.

When there is question of setting up a programme of education in matters of feeding, the collaboration of the people and services who can offer help is indispensable. The local authorities and the health services must be called in aid. As the committee of experts of F.A.O. and W.H.O. has emphasized, it is rather a question of modifying eating habits than of making radical changes: "The only changes which should be sought after are those which the people themselves are able to adopt in practice and to continue to use with the economic and agricultural resources which are at their disposal." This is a very important point and it raises the question of the advisability of making distributions of powdered full cream milk to mothers and children in countries which will not be able to continue to provide such a diet after the temporary aid has come to an end.

In quite a number of the under-developed countries there are now organizations or institutes of nutrition, or nutritional services run by the Ministry of Health, which can undertake the provision of satisfactory educational programmes on nutrition. Such is the case in South and Central America, the Philippines, Indonesia, Malaya and India.[3] These departments have on their staffs nutritionists who are capable of training auxiliary workers and of providing them with all that they may need to teach individuals or groups, making use of visual aids, conference techniques or radio.

There is a wide range of methods which can be used to bring home to people how and why they should change their eating habits. The best are those which engage the interest of the people: discussions, demonstrations, exchanges of views, accompanied by advice to mothers attending maternal and child welfare clinics and practical lessons on the occasion of domestic visits.

There are other audio-visual aids, such as films, handbills, posters and radio talks. These are of use only if they are properly understood and arouse in the public a desire to put the advice which they have received into practice. As a result of some disappointing and expensive experiences, the committee of authorities on questions of nutrition has issued a warning con-

---

[3] Experiments have been made in India to concoct a new, rich food out of products that can be grown in the country: "In February 1957, the Indian Government invited the Swiss expert, M. Charles Hummel, to work at the Food Institute in Mysore on the perfection of a very promising synthetic product. This consists of a mixture of cassava, ground-nut cake and wheat flour, forming a foodstuff complete in itself and rich in vitamins and protein. Cassava can easily be grown on a large scale in India in place of rice or wheat. It yields three times as much starch to the acre as does either of these and its cultivation offers no technical difficulties. As for the ground-nut cake, there is no lack of that in India, since a large part of it is left unused after the ground-nut harvest has been gathered." (*Population* review, Oct. 1957.)

cerning the doubtful advantages of certain methods of popularization:

> It has been the custom to try to educate people by using
> travelling cinema shows, radio talks, articles in the press, or
> even posters in the houses of the village head men or in the
> school class-rooms. The effectiveness of such methods is
> extremely questionable and they should not be used except as
> a means of rounding off the work of a permanent staff.
> Unfortunately, the very large sums which have been devoted
> by governments to the provision of travelling film shows give
> an impression that something has been done, without anyone
> knowing exactly what.[4]

Choice of language is of immense importance when explanations are being given to simple folk. Ullmann remarks that
"the languages of so-called primitive societies are extremely
rich in concrete terms, but singularly poorly provided with
general terms". Thus, a people which feeds largely on rice will
not have a general term for that cereal. It will have one word
for the growing plant, another for the non-husked grain, another
for cooked rice, and so on. Similarly, the Lapps have no general
word for snow, but only a number of different words referring
to each of the forms which snow can take.[5]

The teaching staffs must be alive to the needs and aspirations
of the people. We can quote a typical case from a semi-rural
parish in Vera Cruz, in Mexico. A health centre had recently
been opened there and classes had been organized in child-care,
dressmaking and cookery; and opportunity was taken to give
a free meal to 40 poor children. To the astonishment of the
organizer, within a short time the poor people had ceased to
attend while those who were better off continued to come.
Discreet enquiries revealed the reason. The poor women were
not interested in learning how to cook; what they wanted to be
taught was reading, writing and arithmetic. Their need was
provided for and it was via arithmetic that they came to learn
about cooking and home management. In other cases, the
women made it clear that what they wanted to be taught was
how to sew, not how to cook. Dressmaking lessons formed the

[4] F.A.O.-W.H.O. Joint Committee, *Report of the fourth session*, 1955.
[5] Jelliffe, op. cit.

introduction to what the organizers wanted to teach them. After all, the women believed that they knew all about cooking according to the local custom, while they were acutely conscious of being something less than skilled at dressmaking.[6]

It is sometimes difficult to get housewives to pay any attention to elementary notions of hygiene, since they have no idea of the nature of bacterial or other sources of infection. In Africa, for example, domestic science teachers have to go to great trouble to convince their pupils that they ought to keep their water pots clean and that the water itself, drawn often from a polluted river or cistern, must be boiled before it is given to children to drink or is used in the kitchen. Bad water is the cause of much sickness in Africa.

Well planned special programmes for feeding or for food distribution can do much to improve the nutrition of children and other vulnerable sections of a population. School meals have been provided for a long time now in many countries. By means of them a supplementation of the ordinary diet can be guaranteed to a large number of children, usually by way of a breakfast or mid-morning snack, sometimes consisting of a complete meal.

If the school meal is to serve its purpose well, not only must it have a high nutritional value, but also it must be economical and fairly easy to organize. F.A.O. nutritional experts emphasize the advantage of using domestically produced foodstuffs to the greatest possible extent. A typical example quoted is the "Oslo snack", which was introduced into Norwegian schools before the second world war. The snack consists of sandwiches or biscuits, vitaminized margarine, cream cheese, cod liver paste and a raw carrot, apple or orange according to the time of year. The serving of the meal calls for the minimum of equipment and supervision. The children are given their snack when they arrive at school in the morning, for it is thought that many of them will have had a quite insufficient breakfast before leaving home. It has been established that the children derive more benefit from the snack than they did from the hot meal which used to be served to them.[7]

---

[6] Jelliffe, op. cit.
[7] M. L. Scott, *School meals; their contribution to child health* (F.A.O., 1954).

C.H.—10

Several countries have adapted the "Oslo snack" to their own circumstances. At the Bangio meeting of the Committee on Nutrition in 1948, a pattern for a free meal was agreed upon: the meal was to provide some 400 calories and could be made out of locally available foodstuffs, such as a cereal (rice being very suitable), vegetables, beans or peas and fish.

The value of the Oslo type of school meal has been well established by several studies, particularly those undertaken by Dr Schiotz, professor of hygiene in the University of Oslo. Dr Schiotz studied two groups of children, one of them receiving the "Oslo snack" and the other the traditional hot school dinner. After six weeks it was found that the boys and girls who had been given the "Oslo snack" had made gains in weight 47·7 per cent and 139·8 per cent greater than had the boys and girls in the other group. Similar experiments carried out in Belgium by the National Committee on Nutrition, working under the Ministry of Health, have also produced evidence showing the superiority of school meals of the Oslo type.

Japan is one of the countries which today have a policy for school meals. About 70 per cent of the children there are given either a balanced meal or a nourishing snack at school. This programme is financed entirely by the state, under a special law passed in 1954. Elsewhere, the programmes are on a smaller scale because of lack of resources, despite the help which U.N.I.C.E.F. gives to many countries, primarily in the form of powdered full cream milk.

Apart from the nourishment they afford, school meals have the added value of being a very practical means of training children into good eating habits. It is through the children also that the parents and the general population can be reached, and this is the more true if care is taken to ask for the co-operation of the parents in the establishment of programmes of school feeding. Interest of the parents can be awakened and the risk of the children being fed unsuitably at home is greatly reduced.

For this reason, a warm welcome should be accorded to the programme of nutritional education which has recently been put in hand by the Tunisian government. It is planned to include this subject in all school curricula and to organize demonstrations which will encourage the cultivation of school gardens.

U.N.I.C.E.F. has helped to organize training courses in nutrition for teachers, educational directors and health visitors. At the first of these courses, lasting three days, nearly 800 teachers were given some basic knowledge and a chance to accustom themselves to the use of the audio-visual equipment which has been designed for use in the schools.

As is very well known, milk is one of the best foods for growing children, since it gives them, in an easily digestible form, the essential nutriments of which they have need. A large number of experiments in different countries have brought results which are quite conclusive on this point.[8]

However, milk is scarce, a luxury even, in most under-developed countries; and it is, furthermore, often dangerous in tropical areas because of bad hygiene.[9] No great increase in milk production is to be expected over the greater part of Asia and Africa. It may well be that dairy products will never become a customary food for children in those parts. It has been necessary, therefore, to seek for some alternatives of much the same nutritional value which can serve as the basis of children's diets.

Of late years attention has been concentrated on the edible oils which can be extracted from some leguminous plants, such as the soya bean and the ground nut. A mixture of soya beans, ground nuts and malt makes a "milk" of high nutritional value which is much more agreeable to the taste than is the "milk" of the soya bean by itself. It has long been known that the proteins supplied by cereals and leguminous plants are complementary, but it has been only since the last war that attempts have been made to put this knowledge to some use. Products which mix the two have been used, with good results, in school meals in Indonesia and Chile, as well as in other parts, where factories

[8] We might cite, in particular, the experiments of Corry Mann, in England, and of Tsurumi, in Japan. The latter showed that in the space of six months, children who were given a third of a pint of milk a day made gains in height and weight which were 86 per cent greater than the gains of children in a control group. Tsurumi also found that the children who were given milk had better skin, a fresher colour, were more lively, better students and much better at physical exercises than were the children in the control group.

[9] To quote Balfour: "The method of milking is to suck at the teat or to use hands which are invariably filthy. More often than not, the task immediately prior to milking is to mould the animal's droppings into a cake for fuel. The milk itself is usually put into a pot of baked clay, cracked and the cracks full of dirt, to which flies, ants and cockroaches have easy access."

for manufacturing products which can replace milk have been established with the help of U.N.I.C.E.F.

In those parts of the world where meat is scarce F.A.O. and W.H.O. experts also recommend the use in school meals of foodstuffs based on fish, which has a high content of protein and vitamins in the B group. Small fish can be eaten whole, while there are some fish products, such as fish paste and fish meal, which are rich in calcium.

> From the nutritional point of view, it is of very great importance to include fish or fish products in school menus in countries where the diet is largely vegetarian. Vegetable foods lack vitamin B 12, which is indispensable for growth, while fish has a high content of it.

It is also worth noting that these various substitute products which can be got locally are both nourishing and cheap, whereas liquid milk or powdered full cream milk is expensive if it has to be imported.

A serious problem is posed today by the policy of distributing powdered milk to help the millions of under-fed children which has been followed on a large scale since the war, particularly through U.N.I.C.E.F. The world supply has been coming mainly from Canada and U.S.A. and stocks are becoming exhausted. Apart from that, it may well be asked whether it is wise to introduce a new food on a provisional basis into a country. Such action might serve to turn away the people's attention from their essential task, which is to discover the best way of using the local food resources. Dr Jelliffe has noted that "milk is often quite unconnected with local dietary customs. In Asia and around the Pacific, for example, in normal times milk does not form part of the people's diet." There is an additional risk that mothers will forget how vital it is and natural for them to continue to feed their infants at the breast.

This policy of using up supplies of surplus full cream powdered milk would now seem to be in process of reconsideration and is tending to be used only as a special type of help in certain cases. In this connection we can quote the views of Dr Williams:

In times of crisis it may be necessary to distribute foodstuffs to save human lives, but if there is question of finding a remedy for a chronic condition considerable care in the use of this method will have to be exercised. Sometimes people are ill-informed about the reasons for a distribution and I have seen infants of two months taken from a full breast and put on full cream milk. I have seen children contract xerophthalmia and neither doctor nor nurse notice, so busy have they been in seeing to the distribution of milk.

It is U.N.I.C.E.F. which today does most in the under-developed countries to help on the fight against malnutrition of mothers and children. Since it was formed in 1946, the Children's Fund has used its large resources in 124 countries or territories to assist in the carrying out of 577 projects. It is at the moment assisting in 367 projects in 104 countries or territories. Immediately after the war it took over from U.N.R.R.A. in helping to organize food supplies in twelve European countries. Since then it has extended its activities to the Far East, Latin America and Africa.

The Fund supplies not only full cream powdered milk but also cod liver oil and other foodstuffs which are rich in protein and fats. The principle on which it works is to send only such foods as are of a high nutritional value and can be digested by children and which are also available at moderate prices. The normal practice is to ask the recipient countries to supply local transport and also to match the Fund's gifts with a supply of local produce which is at least equal in calorific value. Personnel and equipment are also expected to be supplied locally to prepare and distribute meals.

Full cream powdered milk has so many advantages as a supplementary article of diet that the demand for it has continued to grow over recent years. This has led the Fund to modify its methods and in particular to offer financial aid to backward countries which will set up plants to preserve milk or to manufacture milk substitutes, such as soya bean "milk" or fish meal. In this way it has helped in the establishment of 31 powdered milk factories, 146 creameries, a fish meal factory, another for making a vegetable extract from the soya bean, another for producing capsules of sharks' liver oil and one for iodizing salt in a campaign against goitre.

U.N.I.C.E.F. works in harmony with the other United Nations organizations, W.H.O. and F.A.O., which are concerned with the health of mothers and children. Together they are engaged on a well balanced plan of campaign, aimed principally at the eradication of malaria, tuberculosis, yaws and trachoma. They help in the development of maternity and child care services. There are now more than 20,000 maternal and child care centres equipped by U.N.I.C.E.F. in all parts of the world, providing a service to 55,000,000 people every year. These centres, which look to the welfare of children of pre-school age, are being more and more followed up with programmes of provision of school meals.

For its part, the F.A.O. helps the under-developed countries with education in matters of nutrition by sending out experts under the technical aid programme. The main beneficiaries of this activity have been Burma, Colombia, Costa Rica, Ecuador, Honduras, Iraq, Iran, Paraguay, Turkey and Tunisia. The aim of the missions to these countries has been to develop education and professional training in nutritional matters, either by the setting up of special programmes of education and supplementary feeding, or by working within the frame of larger enterprises aimed at creating or developing food services. Most of these experts have collaborated in the professional training of local officials by organizing special courses, as we have seen in the case of Tunisia. In addition to this, scholarships have been provided for senior officials to study abroad.

IX

F.A.O. FIGHTS HUNGER

EVER since its beginning in 1946, the F.A.O. has found itself at grips with the problem of hunger. At the end of the second world war most of the countries of Europe were suffering from severe shortages of food and Greece, Italy and Yugoslavia, in particular, appealed to U.N.R.R.A. for help in re-establishing their agriculture.

It was not long before the international organizations found themselves faced with another and even more difficult problem, that of the under-developed countries, and the F.A.O. staff were forced to give more and more of their attention to it. In face of the enormous size and gravity of the food problems of one-third of the world, the F.A.O. stands out as one of the most important organs of the United Nations. It is, indeed, the one which can most contribute to warding off a conflict between the have and the have-not powers.

In the Introduction to the report of the first session of the F.A.O. Congress, the president of the day, Mr Lester B. Pearson, took care to emphasize the eminently social and humanitarian role which had fallen to the young organization.

The first of the new permanent institutions of the United Nations is now established. It represents something entirely new in the field of international affairs and there is little by way of precedent on which it can lean. It is true that there have been international organizations with objectives and tasks which were more or less limited in scope, but the F.A.O. is the first which is so audacious as to aim at the liberation of the peoples of the world from hunger. Never before have the countries of the world come together to attain such an end.

He went on to make clear in what spirit and by what methods the new organization would take care to reach its end and lend aid to all who might ask for it.

The F.A.O. will put the discoveries of science at the disposal of those who are or who may be concerned with questions of feeding, agriculture, forestry and fisheries, while at the same time bringing all their problems in the practical order to the attention of scholars. It will collect, codify and interpret all information which can serve as a basis for the drawing up of national and international policies. It will be able to suggest courses of action, but it is only by the action of governments themselves that the ends in view can be finally attained.

Since 1949, the date of the inception of point four of President Truman's programme, enlarged technical assistance, it has given its very active aid to more than 40 countries which have asked for it. Up to the present time it has organized more than 2,000 missions of experts and has provided almost as large a number of scholarships for the training of foreign technicians, helped financially by the technical assistance fund of the United Nations, which gave about 8,000,000 dollars in 1960. Thanks to the establishment of a special U.N. fund, the F.A.O. has at its disposal another means for aiding the governments of member states which ask for assistance to prepare large scale projects for the development of their resources.

In addition to its task of rendering assistance, the F.A.O. also has the important role of providing an information service. It collects and publishes information from all over the world on questions relating to food and agriculture, its annual statistics on production and trade in the products of agriculture, forestry and fishing being especially valuable. It publishes specialized studies on the most diverse topics: soil conservation, cattle rearing in the tropics, nutrition, water utilization in arid zones, etc. Finally, it organizes numerous international conferences which help governments to plan their policies and programmes for finding solutions to the problems with which they are faced.

The F.A.O. now has fifteen years of experience behind it. It has been able to take the measure of the problems which face it and its constructive action is becoming better understood. As Daniel-Rops has said:

It would be enough in itself to justify the existence of the United Nations. Its real task is to make provision for the means which humanity can bring into service in the fight against hunger and to teach to the peoples of the under-developed countries the techniques which will enable them to feed themselves better.

Despite the efforts which have been made during the last fifteen years to increase the production of foodstuffs, the spectre of hunger and of malnutrition still hangs over a large part of the world. The rapid growth of populations which has been going on in the under-developed countries has made the situation there sometimes worse than it was in 1938.

It is a matter of urgency to use all the means that have been discovered to challenge a situation which threatens the health of entire nations and the peace of the world. This the F.A.O. has well understood. It is for this reason that its Director, Mr Binay Ranjan Sen, an Indian, has taken the initiative and launched, with the support of the member states of U.N., a vast Campaign against Hunger. This campaign, which began in July 1960, and is planned to last for five years, has been carefully prepared and also vetted by the Economic and Social Commission of U.N. Important results can be expected to accrue from it.

Its objectives are, first, to arouse a world opinion which is still too passive in the face of this grievous problem and, second, to instigate activities which will lead to a speedy raising of levels of production and consumption in all those countries where need is great.

Nothing must be neglected in the task of mobilizing throughout the world all men of good will who would wish to have a hand in this task. There is, in particular, the matter of arousing public opinion by means of modern techniques of publicity—press, radio, television, films, etc.—to support and to stimulate government activity and help.

So that the campaign might have the widest possible base, it has been decided to call in aid, in every country, not only official organizations, but also voluntary bodies—organizations and foundations and civic and religious groups which have international connections. Thus, in France, the rural Catholic Action movements have been asked to collaborate actively with the scheme.

This wide scope of the plan should be emphasized, as also the spirit of generous co-operation which has inspired it. The non-governmental organizations will have an important role and it is in large part on their activity that the success of the enterprise will depend. It must be through them that information is spread to the people and from them that the motive power must come to initiate activity, particularly at the national level.

Each country has a national committee, charged with the task of co-ordination, but its operation will vary necessarily from country to country. In some cases, the objective aimed at will be primarily educational and informational; while in others, the emphasis will be primarily on actual plans for improvements in agriculture.

The campaign must be able to dispose of considerable resources if it is to attain its objectives. In many countries the insufficiency of food production is due in part to lack of financial resources for resolving agricultural problems. It is often the case that national governments do not have the funds which are needed to develop the agricultural services, to provide farm credits and to improve the transportation and processing of foodstuffs. At the international level, the F.A.O. has not got funds enough to enable it to extend the scope of its activity as far as would be necessary. One of the duties of the national committees and the non-governmental organizations, mainly in the richer countries, will be to collect funds to meet the expenses of the campaign and provide finance for projects of research and practical action in the backward countries. With this aim in view, a special account has been opened at the headquarters of the F.A.O.

Each national committee will decide for itself the technique which it will use to raise funds for the campaign and its objects. (Some such might be the sale of special stamps, labels and badges and the running of bingo sessions.) Some countries are more aware of these matters than are others. Thus, in Holland the campaign has got off to a very good start: the government has sent a gift of 20,000 dollars to the F.A.O. to help on the work and has launched "Operation Ration-Card". Replicas of the ration cards which were used in that country during the world war, and which remind the Dutch of their sufferings at that time, are sold at 25 Dutch cents by the bakeries at the same

time as they sell their bread. The money thus gathered will go
to meet the costs of a programme of seed selection for wheat
and barley in the Near East.[1]

Large sums have been collected for the fight against hunger
by both Catholics and Protestants in Western Germany. An
appeal by the Catholic bishops raised 32,000,000 marks in 1959,
while preliminary figures showed donations of some 40,000,000
marks in 1960. The Council of the Evangelical Churches has
made an allotment of 7,000,000 marks, 2,000,000 to finance the
campaign and 5,000,000 to help forward agricultural projects
in India, Ceylon, Tanganyika and New Guinea. The World
Congress of Young Farmers (M.I.J.A.R.C.) held at Lourdes in
1960 to consider the theme of hunger in the world has drawn
lively appreciation in France. This great gathering of 25,000
countrymen from all parts of the world cannot be without
result. It is to be hoped that the French National Committee
will do all it can to bring effective aid to the cause of the
campaign.[2]

The campaign is a product of the initiative of the F.A.O. and
will continue to benefit from its help and advice. This is of
great importance, for the Organization now has a precious fund
of world experience—and its services will provide the indispensable co-ordination to help forward the campaign in every
country.

The whole effort of the campaign must be directed towards
constructive ends. It is not simply a matter of supplying a
temporary relief to the under-nourishment of multitudes of
human beings, but of eliminating hunger from the face of the

---

[1] The following are some of the voluntary contributions which have been
made to the special account at the F.A.O. (all sums are in dollars): France,
75,000; Britain, 56,000; Holland, 20,000; Pakistan, 10,000; Denmark, 7,500;
Honduras, 500. Western Germany has announced that from 1961 its contribution will be raised to 100,000 dollars. In addition, the international fertilizer
industry has decided to contribute 2,000,000 dollars over a period of five years
and a first instalment of 130,000 dollars has already been paid.

[2] In France, the *Secours Catholique*, in collaboration with the groups of
Catholic Action, has taken under its wing some enterprises which have been
sponsored by African dioceses. These include, among other projects, rural
training centres and the supplying of tools, farm implements and selected
seed. Thus, the diocese of Carcassonne has adopted a training centre at Piela in
Upper Volta. The Africans themselves say that to help them in their fight
against hunger there is no need for great schemes, but rather for the establishment of quite small training centres where the Christians from the bush
villages can learn how to improve their farming techniques by simple means
which are based upon their traditional way of life.

globe. Even if the surplus farm products of some of the richer countries were to be spread more evenly around the world, they would fall a long way short of meeting the immensity of the need.

From its first *Enquiry into World Nutrition*, the F.A.O. has drawn attention to what it has called the heart of the problem, the necessity of developing the economies of the poorer nations by a combination of appropriate measures.

> The solution to the problem lies in raising people's productivity by equipping them with scientific knowledge and the tools of modern technology. . . . But a high degree of imagination and audacity, in the best sense of that word, are needed to make this knowledge and these tools available to millions of human beings who have never had anything like them. Half-measures are of not the slightest use. A little improvement here, a half-hearted reform there, will lead only to an increase in the numbers of poor and ignorant people, as has happened so often in the past. . . .

The object must be to find all-round solutions, to help countries which lack equipment to produce for themselves that which they lack, so as to profit by the gains of every kind which modern knowledge makes possible.

A high priority must be given to research of different kinds. There will be a multiplication of nutritional studies and field enquiries to provide the first step, exact knowledge of the real needs of every area. It will be necessary to test the directions to give and the methods to use to further agricultural development in different countries. There is a vast field of enquiry to be explored: from the use of fertilizers, improved strains of plants and cattle rearing to the feeding of domestic animals, including chickens and the smaller animals. Included in the programme must also be the organization of farm holdings, provision of farm credits and the marketing of produce.

The various programmes of national action will hold the centre of the stage. It is through them that the measures will be taken which can release whole populations from an obsession with their daily bread. To help forward this part of the programme, the F.A.O. has published a handbook listing the general needs of the under-nourished peoples in the light of the progress that has already been made in the world.[3] The book describes a number of projects which aim at raising food production, the drawing up of agricultural plans and policies, professional training, rural education and governmental agricultural services.

The chapter which describes these last is of considerable importance. It is clear that without permanent structures and well organized services at the national level, such as provision of credit, popularization of farming knowledge, training centres and advisory services, it will be impossible to make lasting progress.

To teach and to guide the rural communities, to advise farmers and help them help themselves, these are among the first things that must be done. The governments themselves must take these duties in hand. The plan provides for the formation at regional level of small teams of people who are able to make knowledge available in a popular form. It will be their task to set up and to direct the working of small "schools" which will provide training to the senior officials of the governmental departments which are concerned with farm problems and questions of rural development. These "schools" will be followed up by an exchange of views and should lead to the adoption of clear plans for strengthening the agricultural services in each country and for getting the governments to take the necessary measures. Part of the costs of this will fall upon the governments concerned, while the organizers of the campaign against hunger will meet the costs of the teams sent out to conduct the "schools". It is expected that this part of the plan will take from three to four years, depending upon the number of countries which take part in it.

Also urgent is the task of finding a solution to the problems of providing credit and markets for agricultural produce in the under-developed countries. If farmers are to undertake investments, they must be backed up by a credit institution which will remove the necessity of going to the money lenders. In the same way, great encouragement and support can be given to productive effort if channels of distribution are organized, with provision for storing the harvests and for standardizing and processing some of the crops. The aim is to encourage the

[3] *Choice of national projects*, F.A.O.

foundation of credit institutions and to develop those which already exist in the under-developed countries. It has been observed that to tie in credit provision with storage of crops makes possible a very flexible system. The produce in the warehouses provides collateral for loans to the small farmers, who will be enabled in this way to buy better tools, selected seeds and fertilizers.

The carrying out of this project would be done in two stages. It would be necessary first of all to make a pilot study in a particular area of the existing facilities for the provision of credit and organization of markets. This study would call for the recruiting and training of investigators, and it would be only after they had collected the information that the appropriate recommendations for policy could be made and steps taken to bring in the appropriate legislative measures.

Among the measures which have been proposed to increase production are price guarantees to farmers, subsidies for equipment and raw materials, credit at low interest rates and on easier terms, and preferential taxation treatment. We must not lose sight of the fact that it is also essential to raise the standard of professional competence among farmers. There are various ways in which this might be done. A start can be made with children, familiarizing them with the elements by the aid of school gardens. Farm manuals can be prepared in the local languages and training centres set up to provide for different levels of professional training.

The problem of providing professional training for farmers ought to be given particular attention in the under-developed countries, since agriculture remains the dominant and most widespread activity in most of them. It would seem to be necessary to look to a two-fold objective in this regard:

First, to give elementary training to the mass of country dwellers to get them to improve their productive methods;

Secondly, to provide a more advanced training for the staffs of the agricultural services and also for those who want to become really expert in farm matters.

X

CONCLUSION

HUNGER has not yet been conquered. Over the face of the world there are still large dark patches which now, in this day of progress, remind us in many ways of the less successful periods of man's history, when wretchedness and want and a perpetual uncertainty as to when next they would eat were the common lot of all mankind.

There is one difference today. Now we know, beyond any shadow of doubt, that this situation can be remedied. The earth can feed its inhabitants. Even though the population grows each year by some fifty millions, the people can also enormously extend their command over the world they inhabit and the life upon it. Although there are some who fear otherwise, for a long time to come it will still be possible to maintain a balance between population and the means of life. Neither land nor technical resources are deficient. At no other time have we been able to dispose of such powerful means and such large resources. All that is necessary is that men should at last decide to get together and to collaborate unreservedly. If they will do this, within the space of a few years the growth of world output will be such as to put an end to the tragedy which bears so heavily on the conscience of so many people.

It is true, as we have shown, that efforts have been made on both a national and an international scale to bring help to the poorer countries, by sending them trained men and equipment and often also considerable financial aid. At the same time, no one can deny that this assistance is far from being enough to meet the need and stands in sharp contrast with the fantastic sums, larger by thirty or forty times, which are spent on armaments. There is no lack of money for killing men: but up to the present time, we have not succeeded in getting together the funds which would be required to keep men alive.

This insufferable paradox cannot continue indefinitely. The day must come when it will provoke such a revolutionary change in the conscience of the world that the solution to the problem will impose itself.

For the most part, the under-developed countries are in only an embryonic stage of economic development and have no lack of potential resources. They have the land and water to grow crops and rear cattle but often lack the knowledge to make their resources fruitful. The rate of increase of their populations, higher now than it was formerly, does not appear to present an insurmountable obstacle: on the contrary, it can, in many cases, become a precious help.

It must not be supposed that the agricultural surpluses which some countries have available can supply the immensity of the world's needs. They could never supply more than a measure of provisional aid which would be particularly welcome where needs were urgent. The true solution is one which would be at the same time both the most truly human and the most strictly economic—to help these late starters among us to help themselves by teaching them how to produce greater quantities of the food they need and in better conditions.

This is a many sided problem. We have tried in these pages to point to the many difficulties and have not played down the obstacles of all kinds which have to be surmounted. It is obvious that it will be most difficult to induce peoples who are 80 to 90 per cent illiterate to modernize their agricultural techniques. Nevertheless, in the circumstances of today there is not one of the problems this task presents for which a satisfactory solution cannot be found.

Meanwhile, it is our duty to remain alert and watchful that no chance is lost to feed the people. As M. Louis Estrangin said so clearly at the Angers *Semaine Sociale*,[1] the problem of food in the world is very pressing.

We would be in grave danger if this state of affairs did not worry us. It will be a human tragedy if the question is not properly resolved on a world scale. If the non-Communist part of the world finds no real solution to it—and if the

[1] Louis Estrangin, "La Faim du Monde et l'avenir des économies agricoles", *Semaine Sociale d'Angers*, 1959.

Chinese method of dealing with it should appear to be the only efficacious way—there will be a political and a spiritual tragedy, too.

For both technical and political reasons, the question which faces us becomes less and less a local problem. Methods which aim at self-sufficiency, even regional self-sufficiency, are already being questioned. Soon, national self-sufficiency, the self-sufficiency of the 90 or 100 units which are called "nations", will also appear to be totally irrational and out-dated. Soon we shall be forced to recognize the need to move towards making concerted plans for agriculture on a world scale. It is to be hoped that we shall be able to help in this reform by turning our minds and our efforts in that direction.

The task which faces this generation is gigantic. Its solution calls for the co-operation of everybody. Our divisions and the changing fortunes of the cold war may well appear to our descendants as paltry squabbles, in comparison with the imperative duty which is laid today on all mankind—that of seeing that men are fed.

As Josué de Castro has truly said: "Hunger is not something which is natural and inevitable: it is a problem of the moral order." It is a social problem of the highest importance and one, therefore, to which men must find an answer.

BIBLIOGRAPHY*

(1) FOOD PRODUCTION AND POPULATION GROWTH

ANDERSON, S. W., *Population Growth and Capital Requirements in Underdeveloped Countries* (U.N., New York, 1955).

BELSHAW, H., *Population Growth and Levels of Consumption* (London, Allen & Unwin, and New York, Inst. of Public Relations, 1956).

BOYD-ORR, John, and LUBBOCK, David, *The White Man's Dilemma*, (London, Allen and Unwin, 1953).

CALDER, R., *Commonsense about a Starving World*, London, Gollancz, 1962).

CLARK, C., *Natural Resources and World Population* (The work of the Scientific Conference of the U.N. for the conservation and exploitation of natural resources).

COALE, A. J., and HOOVER, E. M., *Population Growth and Economic Development in Low Income Countries* (Princeton University Press, Princeton, 1959).

FAGLEY, Richard M., *The Population Explosion and Christian Responsibility* (Princeton University Press, Princeton, 1960).

FARIS, Donald, *To Plough with Hope* (London, Victor Gollancz, and New York, Harper, 1958).

HOFFMAN, P. G., *One Hundred Countries, One and one quarter billion people* (U.N. Association).

LESTAPIS, S. de, S.J., *Family Planning and Modern Problems* (London, Burns & Oates, and New York, Herder, 1961).

McCORMACK, Arthur, *People, Space, Food* (London, Sheed and Ward, 1960).

NEVETT, Albert, S.J., *Are we too many?* (St. Paul Publications, Allahabad and Bombay, 1957).

PIERRE, Abbé, *Man is Your Brother* (London, Geoffrey Chapman, and Notre Dame, Ind., Fides, 1958).

ROSTOW, W. W., *The Stages of Economic Growth* (C.U.P., New York, 1960).

RUSSELL, Sir J., *World Population and Food Supplies* (London, Allen and Unwin, 1954).

RUSSELL, Sir J., and WRIGHT, Dr. Norman (Joint Editors), *Hunger, Can it be Averted?* (Papers read at the Cardiff Symposium, 1960; from the British Association for the Advancement of Science, London).

*This Bibliography is based on that provided for the Study Course "Freedom from Hunger" for the Newman Association Discussion Groups. The Publishers are grateful to the Newman Association for their co-operation, and to the Rev. Arthur McCormack for additional suggestions.

SAUVY, A., *Fertility and Survival* (London, Chatto & Windus, and New York, Criterion, 1961).
SPAULL, Hebe, *The World Unites against Want* (London, Barrie and Rockliffe, 1961).
United Nations Study, No. 28: *The Future Growth of World Population* (U.N., New York, 1960).
ZIMMERMAN, A., *Overpopulation* (Washington, Catholic Univ. of America Press, 1957); *The Catholic Viewpoint on Overpopulation* (New York, Doubleday, 1961).

(2) WORLD PATTERN OF INCOME DISTRIBUTION AND RESOURCES

VINER, J., *International Trade and Economic Development* (London, O.U.P., and New York, Free Press Glencoe, 1957).
WARD, Barbara, *India and the West* (London, Hamish Hamilton, and New York, Norton, 1961).

United Nations Publications:
Economic Bulletin for Asia and the Far East, Vol. 8, No. 4 (Bangkok, 1958).
Preliminary Report on World Social Situation (New York, 1952).
Report on World Social Situation (New York, 1957).

F.A.O. Publications:
Agriculture in the World Economy (Rome, 1955).
National Food Reserve Policies in Underdeveloped Countries (Rome, 1958).

(3) DIET AND HEALTH

BENNETT, M. K., *The World's Food* (Harper, New York, 1954).
LEE, D. H. K., *Climate and Economic Development in the Tropics* (London and New York, O.U.P., 1957).
OSER, Jacob, *Must Men Starve?* (London, J. Cape; New York, Abelard-Schuman, 1956).
SCHLIPPE, P. de., *Shifting Cultivation in Africa* (London, Routledge, and New York, Humanities Press, 1956).

F.A.O. Publications:
Calory Requirements, Report of the 2nd Committee (Rome, 1957).
Dietary Surveys: Their Techniques and Interpretation (Rome, 1949).
F.A.O. and World Health Organisation Seminar on Problems of Food and Nutrition in Africa, South of the Sahara (Rome, 1961).
Maize and Rice Diets (Rome, 1953–54).
Nutrition and Society (World Food Problems No. 1).
Nutrition Problems of Rice Eating Countries in Asia (Rome, 1948).
Protein Requirements (Rome, 1958).
Report of the Nutrition Committee for South and East Asia, 1950, 1953, 1956.
Report of Third Conference on Nutrition Problems in Latin America, 1953–54.

Reports of Joint F.A.O./W.H.O. Committee on Nutrition, 1951, 1952, 1954, 1957.

Rice and Rice Diets (Rome, 1954).

AUTRET, M., and BEHAR, M., *Sindrome Policarencial Infantil (Kwashiorkor) and its Prevention in Central America* (Rome, 1955).

BROCK, J. F., and AUTRET, M., *Kwashiorkor in Africa* (Rome, 1952).

KON, S. K., *Milk and Milk Products in Human Nutrition* (Rome, 1959).

SCOTT, M. L., *School Feeding: Its Contribution to Child Nutrition* (Rome, 1954).

WATERLOW, J., and VERGARA, A., *Protein Malnutrition in Brazil* (Rome, 1957).

(4) SCIENTIFIC AND TECHNICAL POSSIBILITIES IN AGRICULTURE

Span (Shell International Chemical Co. Ltd., London), Vol. IV, 1, 1961.
  (i) " Food for Thought ".
  (ii) R. B. Sen—" Towards Freedom from Hunger ".
  (iii) L. D. Stamp—" People, Land and Reclamation ".
  (iv) M. McG. Cooper—" More Food from Grassland ".
  (v) C. P. McMeekan—" More Food from Livestock ".
  (vi) N. W. Pirie—" More Protein Food from Plants: The Field Surveyed ".
  (vii) A. G. Van Veen and R. O. Whyte—" More Protein Food from Plants, Pulses and Processed Foods ".
  (viii) J. B. Harrington—" Wheat and Barley Improvements in the Near East ".
  (ix) D. H. Grist—" Developments in the Rice Industry ".
  (x) P. Allan—" Fertilisers and Food in Asia and the Far East ".
  (xi) G. Ordish—" More Food by Crop Protection ".
  (xii) G. V. B. Herford—" Food lost in store by Insect Attack ".
  (xiii) D. C. Kimmel—" The Need for Efficient Extension Services ".

F.A.O. Publications:

Improving Livestock under Tropical and Subtropical Conditions (Rome, 1960).

Inter-relationship between Agrarian Reform and Agricultural Development (Rome, 1953).

Soil Conservation: An International Study (Rome, 1943).

Soil Erosion by Wind and Measures for its Control in Agricultural Lands.

HOPFEN, H. J., *Farm Implements for Arid and Tropical Regions* (Rome, 1960).

RAMIAH, K., *Factors Affecting Rice Production* (Rome, 1955).

SEMPLE, A. T., *Improving the World's Grasslands* (Rome, 1956).

VAYDAY, A. de, *Some Aspects of Surface-Water Development in Arid Regions* (Rome, 1953).

(5) POTENTIAL OF THE OCEANS AND THE ATMOSPHERE

F.A.O. Publication: *Fish—The Great Potential Food Supply*—No. 3 in series on *World Food Problems*.
PROWSE, G. A., " More Food from Fish ", in *Span* (Shell International Chemical Co., London), Vol. IV, 1, 1961.

(6) COSTS AND DIFFICULTIES IN APPLYING SOLUTIONS

ARGAWALA and SINGH (Editors), *The Economics of Underdevelopment* (O.U.P., India, 1958).
BAUER, P. T., and YAMEY, B. S., *The Economics of Underdeveloped Countries*, Camb. Econ. Hdbks. (London, Nisbet, 1957).
BENHAM, F., *Economic Aid to the Underdeveloped Countries* (O.U.P., London, 1961).
HIRSCHMAN, A. O., *The Strategy of Economic Development* (London and New York, Yale University Press, 1958).
HOSELITZ, B. F. (Ed.), *The Progress of Underdeveloped Areas:* East Africa Royal Commission 1953–55 Report (Parliamentary Paper Cmd., 9475, 1955).
KINDLEBERGER, C. P., *Economic Development* (McGraw-Hill, London and New York, 1958).
KNOX, A. D., " Problems of Economic Growth in the Underdeveloped Countries " (*Bankers Magazine*, January 1961).
LEIBENSTEIN, H., *Economic Backwardness and Economic Growth* (New York, Wiley, 1957).
LEWIS, W. A., *The Theory of Economic Growth* (London, Allen & Unwin, and Homewood, Ill., Richard Irwin, 1955).
MEIER, G. M, and BALDWIN, R. E., *Economic Development* (New York, Wiley, 1957).
MYRDAL, G., *Economic Theory and Underdeveloped Regions* (London, Duckworth); *Rich Lands and Poor* (New York, Harper, 1958).
NURKSE, R., *Problems of Capital Formation in Underdeveloped Countries* (Oxford, Blackwell, 1957).
SHONFIELD, A., *The Attack on World Poverty* (London, Chatto & Windus, 1960).
STAMP, L. D., *Our Developing World* (London, Faber, 1960).
WARRINER, D., *Land Reform and Development in the Middle East* (London, O.U.P., 1957).

United Nations Publications (New York):
Land Reform: Defects in Agrarian Structure as Obstacles to Economic Development (1951).
Progress in Land Reform, Second Report (1956).
Social Progress through Community Development (1955).

F.A.O. Publication (Rome): *Activities of F.A.O. under the Expanded Technical Assistance Programme* (1955).

Inter-African Labour Institute (Brazzaville, Congo): *The Human Factors of Productivity in Africa*.

(7) INTERNATIONAL CO-OPERATION FOR FREEDOM FROM HUNGER

HAMBRIDGE, G., *The Story of F.A.O.* (Toronto, Van Nostrand, 1955).

F.A.O. Publications (Rome):

Man and Hunger; World Food Problems Series No. 2 (1957).

Millions Still go Hungry (1957).

National Action Projects, A selection (1960).

Second World Food Survey (1952). (A statistical survey of the nutrition of the world population. The Third World Food Survey is in preparation.)

The State of Food and Agriculture, 1960.

YATES, P. Lamartine, *So Bold an Aim; Ten Years of International Co-operation toward Freedom from Want* (1955).

U.N.E.S.C.O. Publications (Paris):

MEAD, Margaret, *Cultural Patterns and Technical Change* (1953).

Social Implications of Industrialisation and Urbanisation in Africa, South of the Sahara (1956).

NIHIL OBSTAT : JOANNES M. T. BARTON, S.T.D., L.S.S.

CENSOR DEPUTATUS

IMPRIMATUR : E. MORROGH BERNARD

VICARIUS GENERALIS

WESTMONASTERII : DIE 9a MAII 1962

The Nihil obstat *and* Imprimatur *are a declaration that a book or pamphlet is considered to be free from doctrinal or moral error. It is not implied that those who have granted the* Nihil obstat *and* Imprimatur *agree with the contents, opinions or statements expressed.*

INDEX